Essential SQA EXAM PRACTICE

MATHEMATICS

Practice Questions & Exam Papers

QUESTIONS & PAPERS

NATIONAL 5

Practise **160+ questions** covering every question type and topic

Complete **2 practice papers** that mirror the real SQA exams

Mike Smith

HODDER GIBSON
AN HACHETTE UK COMPANY

Orders: please contact Hachette UK Distribution, Hely Hutchinson Centre, Milton Road, Didcot, Oxfordshire, OX11 7HH. Telephone: +44 (0)1235 827827. Email: education@hachette.co.uk. Lines are open from 9 a.m. to 5 p.m., Monday to Friday. You can also order through our website: www.hoddereducation.co.uk. If you have queries or questions that aren't about an order, you can contact us at hoddergibson@hodder.co.uk

© Mike Smith 2019

First published in 2019 by

Hodder Gibson, an imprint of Hodder Education

An Hachette UK Company

50 Frederick Street

Edinburgh, EH2 1EX

Impression number   5   4   3   2
Year   2023   2022

Illustrations by Aptara Inc.

Typeset by Aptara Inc.

Printed and bound by CPI Group (UK) Ltd, Croydon CR0 4YY

A catalogue record for this title is available from the British Library.

ISBN: 978 1 5104 7189 4

We are an approved supplier on the Scotland Excel framework.

Find us on your school's procurement system as

Hachette UK Distribution Ltd or Hodder & Stoughton Limited t/a Hodder Education.

MIX

Paper | Supporting responsible forestry

FSC™ C104740

CONTENTS

INTRODUCTION

National 5 Mathematics

Welcome to this set of Practice Questions and Papers, designed to give you experience in the types of questions, the format of question papers, and how to set out your solutions to gain full marks in your National 5 Mathematics exam.

Structure of the book

The questions in the book are split into two main sections. The first section contains groups of Practice Questions arranged by topic. The second section contains two sets of full Practice Papers. This structure provides you with the opportunity to focus your revision on individual topics as well as completing full practice assessments.

The book also contains:

▶ the Formulae List provided for the SQA National 5 Mathematics examination

▶ an Answers section containing fully worked answers and marking instructions for all questions in the book

▶ Practice Questions Key Skills index grid

▶ Practice Papers Key Skills index grid.

The questions in both sections provide comprehensive coverage of the course content and are similar to the type of questions that will appear in the final examination, in line with the 2019 course assessment. The Practice Papers mirror the format of Paper 1 and Paper 2 of the final examination.

Features in the book

The Practice Questions section features:

▶ Top tips on how to tackle many of the questions

▶ Hints for answering the questions

▶ an icon ▦ indicating which questions require the use of a calculator.

Questions which do not have this icon attached to them should be done without a calculator. Such questions could appear on either Paper 1 or Paper 2 of the exam.

The Answers sections for both the Practice Questions and the Practice Papers feature:

▶ the 'Grade demand' of each question (C = level C; > C = above level C)

▶ commentary, hints and tips explaining the answers.

Know your course

The course will help you to develop skills, techniques and knowledge which you will apply to problems to show understanding. These are known as 'operational' skills.

You will also develop 'reasoning' skills to help you to 'think your way' through a problem.

Know your exam

Your grade for the course is determined by your performance in the course assessment – the exam. This exam will test skills beyond the minimum competence required for success in the free-standing Units.

The course is graded A to D, the grade being determined by the total mark you achieve in the final exam. Your exam is structured as follows:

Paper 1 (non-calculator)	1 hour 15 minutes	50 marks
Paper 2 (calculator allowed)	1 hour 50 minutes	60 marks
Totals	3 hours 05 minutes	110 marks

Know how to prepare

Mathematics should be regarded as a VERB; that is, it is a **DOING** WORD! Doing mathematics questions is the best use of your study time – practice makes perfect! You will benefit a lot more from doing questions than reading notes or copying from a textbook.

When DOING questions, practise showing **ALL YOUR WORKING**. Instructions in the exam papers clearly state that 'Full credit will only be given where the solution contains appropriate working'.

Attempt every question, and every part of every question. Even if you cannot do one part of a question, you may still be able to do another part – so do not give up!

Do not leave blanks – write something down, as all working has to be checked and there may be a line worth a mark or two. Never score out working unless you have replaced it with something better.

A method that some use while answering questions is the '**CUBE**' method, shown below.

C	**Circle** the **COMMAND** word(s)
	Write down, State, Calculate, Determine, Show that, Will the ...
U	**Underline** the **KEY WORD**(s) or phrases
	Increase in value, standard deviation, system of equations, parabola ...
B	**Box** the **NUMBERS**
	Put a box round any numbers given to highlight: increase of 5%, 32×10^4 ...
E	**Explain** your **ANSWER**
	For example, if it is a volume question, don't just say $x = 40$, write volume = 40 cm^3, that is, give context.

Key Area index grids

The Key Area index grids on pages vi and vii show how the course content is spread across the Practice Questions and Practice Papers sections. You can use these if you want to do a part or complete paper.

Revision

You can download a Revision Calendar to use as part of your studies from our website at www.hoddergibson.co.uk/ESEP-extras.

Good luck in your revision and your final National 5 Mathematics exam!

FORMULAE LIST

The roots of	$ax^2 + bx + c = 0$ are $x = \dfrac{-b \pm \sqrt{(b^2 - 4ac)}}{2a}$
Sine rule:	$\dfrac{a}{\sin A} = \dfrac{b}{\sin B} = \dfrac{c}{\sin C}$
Cosine rule:	$a^2 = b^2 + c^2 - 2bc\cos A$ or $\cos A = \dfrac{b^2 + c^2 - a^2}{2bc}$
Area of a triangle:	$A = \dfrac{1}{2}ab\sin C$
Volume of a sphere:	$V = \dfrac{4}{3}\pi r^3$
Volume of a cone:	$V = \dfrac{1}{3}\pi r^2 h$
Volume of a pyramid:	$V = \dfrac{1}{3}Ah$
Standard deviation:	$s = \sqrt{\dfrac{\Sigma(x - \bar{x})^2}{n-1}}$
or	$s = \sqrt{\dfrac{\Sigma x^2 - \dfrac{(\Sigma x)^2}{n}}{n-1}}$ where n is the sample size.

Practice Questions

The skills and subskills are shown in the Key Skills index grid below. The grid also shows the Practice Questions (PQ) which deal with each subskill. You can use this grid if you want to focus on practising a particular topic.

Algebraic skills		Geometric skills	
Subskill	**PQ**	**Subskill**	**PQ**
Expanding brackets and simplifying	1–10	Arcs and sectors	1–6
Factorising and completing the square	11–20	Volume of standard and composite solids	7–10
Algebraic fractions	21–30	Applying Pythagoras' theorem	11–17
Find / interpret the equation of a straight line	31–35	Circles and polygons	18–20
Solve linear equations and inequations	36–43	Similarity	21–25
Solve simultaneous equations	44–49	2D and 3D vectors	26–30
Change the subject of a formula	50–55		
Quadratic function: graphs	56–60		
Quadratic equations; factorising, using the formula and the discriminant	61–70		
Trigonometric skills		**Statistical and numerical skills**	
Subskill	**PQ**	**Subskill**	**PQ**
Graphs of trigonometric functions	1–4	Surds	1–6
Trig equations and identities	5–11	Indices	7–14
Area of a triangle using trigonometry	12–14	Percentages	15–24
Sine and cosine rules	15–21	Fractions and mixed numbers	25–30
Using bearings with trigonometry	22–27	Standard deviation and interquartile range	31–35
		Scattergraphs	36, 37

Practice Papers

This Key Skills index grid shows the questions in the Practice Papers which deal with each subskill. You can use this grid if you want to do a whole or a part of a Practice Paper.

Skill	Subskill	Practice Paper A1	A2	B1	B2
Algebraic	Manipulate algebraic expressions *Brackets* *Factorising* *Change subject*	2 4 7 14 16		2 4 6	
Algebraic	Algebraic fractions	10		9 16	
Algebraic	Straight line	15	14	13 17	2
Algebraic	Equations and inequations	3 11		8 14	
Algebraic	Quadratic functions	8	4		
Algebraic	Quadratic equations	6 13			5
Geometric	Use of formulae *Arcs / sectors* *Pythagoras in circle* *Volume*		6 11	7	3 7 13
Geometric	Pythagoras' theorem		12	5	15
Geometric	Properties of circles / polygons				13
Geometric	Similarity				9
Geometric	Vectors	5 12	3	15	11
Trigonometric	Trig graphs, identities, and equations	17 18	10 15	12	4 10
Trigonometric	Non right-angled triangles *Area* *Sine / cosine rules* *Bearings*		5 8 3	11	8 14 16
Statistical and Numerical	Surds and indices	5 9	2	3 5 10	1
Statistical and Numerical	Percentages		1 7		12
Statistical and Numerical	Decimals and fractions	1		1	
Statistical and Numerical	Analyse data *Mean and standard deviation* *Semi-interquartile range*		9		6
Statistical and Numerical	Scattergraph / line of best fit		14		

Algebraic skills

≫ HOW TO ANSWER

Expanding brackets and simplifying

Expand $(2x + 3)(3x^2 + 4x - 2)$.

$$2x(3x^2 + 4x - 2) + 3(3x^2 + 4x - 2) = 6x^3 + 8x^2 - 4x + 9x^2 + 12x - 6$$
$$= 6x^3 + 17x^2 + 8x - 6$$

Top Tip!

For this type of question, split the two-term bracket then multiply the second bracket by each of these terms.

		MARKS
1	Expand and simplify $(3x + 2)(3x - 5)$.	2
2	Expand and simplify $(3x - 2)(2x + 5)$.	2
3	Expand and simplify $(4k - y)(3k + 5y)$.	2
4	Expand and simplify $4(3x - 1) - 5(2x + 3)$.	3
5	Expand and simplify $(3x - 5)^2$.	2
6	Expand and simplify $(3x + 2)^2 + 5(3x - 2)$.	3
7	Expand and simplify $(3x - 2)(4x + 1) + 2(3x^2 + 1)$.	3
8	Expand and simplify $(2x + 3)(2x^2 + 3x + 1)$.	3
9	Expand and simplify $(3x - 2)(4x^2 + 5x - 3)$.	3
10	Expand and simplify $(4x^2 - 2x + 5)(3x - 2)$.	3

≫ HOW TO ANSWER

Factorising and completing the square

Factorise $8x^2 - 50$.

$$8x^2 - 50 = 2(4x^2 - 25)$$
$$= 2[(2x)^2 - 5^2]$$
$$= 2(2x - 5)(2x + 5)$$

Top Tip!

Take out common factor.
Set up as difference of two squares.

		MARKS
11	Factorise $3x^2 - 18x$.	2
12	Factorise $6x^2 - 9x$.	2
13	Factorise $x^2 - 64$.	1
14	Factorise $9a^2 - 4b^2$.	2
15	Factorise $x^2 + 8x + 15$.	2
16	Factorise $x^2 - 3x - 4$.	2
17	Factorise $3x^2 - 11x - 4$.	2
18	Factorise $6x^2 - 11x - 10$.	2
19	Express $x^2 + 8x + 12$ in the form $(x + a)^2 - b$.	3
20	Express $x^2 - 4x + 1$ in the form $(x - a)^2 - b$.	3

≫ HOW TO ANSWER

Algebraic fractions

Simplify $\dfrac{x^2 + 8x + 15}{x + 3}$

$x^2 + 8x + 15 = (x + 5)(x + 3)$

$\dfrac{(x + 5)(x + 3)}{x + 3} = x + 5$

Solve the equation $\dfrac{2x + 1}{3} - \dfrac{x}{4} = 2$

$4(2x + 1) - 3x = 24$

$8x + 4 - 3x = 24$

$5x + 4 = 24$

$x = 4$

Top Tip!

Factorise numerator.

Cancel $(x + 3)$.

Top Tip!

Multiply by 12 to eliminate fractions.

Expand bracket.

Collect like terms and solve.

MARKS

21 Express as a single fraction in its simplest form $\dfrac{1}{3x} - \dfrac{1}{4x}$; $x \neq 0$. **2**

22 Express as a single fraction in its simplest form $\dfrac{4}{x} - \dfrac{3 - x}{x^2}$; $x \neq 0$. **3**

23 Express as a single fraction in its simplest terms $\dfrac{5}{x} + \dfrac{2}{(x - 2)}$; $x \neq 0, x \neq 2$. **3**

24 a) Factorise $4a^2 - b^2$. **1**

   b) Hence simplify $\dfrac{4a^2 - b^2}{8a - 4b}$ **2**

25 a) Factorise $x^2 + x - 6$. **1**

   b) Hence simplify $\dfrac{x^2 + x - 6}{(x + 3)^2}$ **2**

26 Simplify $\dfrac{x^2 + 8x + 12}{(x + 2)}$ **3**

27 Simplify $\dfrac{x - 2}{3} \div \dfrac{x^2 - 4}{3}$ **3**

28 Solve **algebraically** the equation $\dfrac{x - 4}{2} - \dfrac{x + 1}{3} = 1$ **3**

29 Solve **algebraically** the equation $\dfrac{x - 3}{2} + \dfrac{2x - 1}{3} = 4$ **4**

30 Solve this equation for x: $\dfrac{x - 2}{3} - \dfrac{x}{2} = \dfrac{1}{4}$ **4**

≫ HOW TO ANSWER

Find/interpret the equation of a straight line

The cost of a journey with Mike's Minicabs depends on the distance travelled.

The graph shows the cost, P pounds, of a journey with Mike's Minicabs against the distance travelled, d miles.

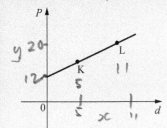

$$x_1, y_1$$
$$(5, 12) \quad (11, 20)$$
$$x_2 \quad y_2$$

$$y = mx + c$$

Kevin's journey, represented by point K, was 5 miles and cost £12.

Leanne's journey, represented by point L, was 11 miles and cost £20.

a) Find the equation of the line in terms of P and d.

Give the equation in its simplest form.

b) Find the cost of Jane's journey, a distance of 2 miles.

a
$$m = \frac{y_2 - y_1}{x_2 - x_1}$$

$$= \frac{20 - 12}{11 - 5}$$

$$= \frac{8}{6} = \frac{4}{3} \checkmark$$

$$y = mx + c$$

$$y - 12 = \frac{4}{3}(x - 5)$$

$$3y - 36 = 4x - 20$$

$$3y = 4x + 16$$

$$3P = 4d + 16$$

In terms of P and d: $3P = 4d + 16$

b
$$3P = 4d + 16$$

$$= 4(2) + 16$$

$$= 24$$

$$P = 8$$

Jane's journey costs £8.

> **Top Tip!**
> Work out m using information for K and L.

> **Top Tip!**
> Substitute $m = \frac{4}{3}$ and point $(5, 12)$ into $y - b = m(x - a)$.
> Multiply through by 3.

> **Top Tip!**
> Use correct labels.

> **Top Tip!**
> Substitute $d = 2$.

$$y - b = m(x - a)$$
$$m = \text{gradient}$$
$$a, b \text{ is a point}$$

31 Find the equation of this line in the form $y = mx + c$. **3**

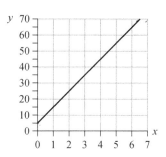

32 A water tank contains 5 litres of water. **3**

The graph shows how the volume of water changes as a further 35 litres of water is pumped into the tank at a steady rate over a period of 60 seconds.

Find the equation of the straight line in terms of V and t.

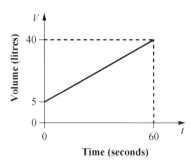

33 The scattergraph shows the marks of a class of students who sat a history and a geography test. **3**

A line of best fit, AB, has been drawn.

Point A represents a student who scored 0 for history and 11 for geography.

Point B represents a student who scored 90 for history and 81 for geography.

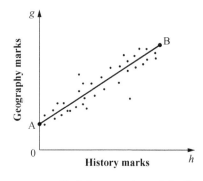

    a) Find the equation of the line of best fit in terms of g and h. **3**

    b) Student C scored 54 marks in her history test. **1**

        She was absent for the geography test.

        Use your answer in part (a) to estimate her mark for the geography test.

34 Find the equation of the straight line joining the points $(-1, 6)$ and $(3, 24)$. **3**

Give the equation in its simplest form.

35   **a)** A straight line has equation $3x + 4y = 20$. **2**

        Find the gradient of this straight line.

    b) Find the coordinates of the point where this line crosses the x-axis. **2**

≫ HOW TO ANSWER

Solve linear equations and inequations

Solve the equation $5 - 2(1 + 3x) = 27$.

$5 - 2(1 + 3x) = 27$

$5 - 2 - 6x = 27$

$3 - 6x = 27$

$-6x = 24$

$x = -4$

Check: LHS $= 5 - 2(1 + 3(-4))$

$= 5 - 2(-11)$

$= 5 + 22$

$= 27 = $ RHS ✓

Top Tip!

Multiply out bracket.

Subtract 3 from both sides.

Divide both sides by 6.

Top Tip!

It's good practice to check your solution by substituting it back into the left-hand side of the original equation and checking it equals the right-hand side.

MARKS

36	Solve the equation $10 - 3(x + 1) = 4$.	3
37	Solve the equation $5 + 3b = b - 15$.	3
38	Solve the equation $6(x + 1) - 2x = x + 3$.	3
39	Solve the equation $\dfrac{3}{x} + 2 = 7$.	3
40	Solve the inequality $3y < 5 - (y + 1)$.	3
41	Solve the inequality $3 - (x - 5) \geq 3x$.	3
42	Solve the inequality $6x - 2 > 5(1 - 3x)$.	3
43	Solve the inequality $2 + 5x \leq 8x - 16$.	3

» HOW TO ANSWER

Solve simultaneous equations

Four coffees and three scones cost £16·50.

Two coffees and four scones cost £12.

Form a system of equations and solve them to find the cost of one coffee and one scone.

Letting c stand for coffee and s stand for scone gives

$4c + 3s = 16.50$ ①

$2c + 4s = 12$ ②

$4c + 8s = 24$ ③

$5s = 7.50$

$s = 1.50$

One scone costs £1·50.

$4c + 3(1.50) = 16.50$

$4c + 4.50 = 16.50$

$4c = 12$

$c = 3$

One coffee costs £3.

One coffee and one scone cost £4·50.

> **Top Tip!**
> Multiply ② by 2.
> Subtract ③ − ①.

> **Top Tip!**
> Substitute cost of one scone into ①.

MARKS

44 Solve this pair of simultaneous equations.   **2**

$2x + y = 9$

$x - y = 3$

45 Solve for x and y.   **3**

$2x + 3y = 5$

$7x + 4y = -2$

46 Four peaches and three apricots cost £1·30.

a) Write down an algebraic equation to illustrate this.   **1**

Two peaches and four apricots cost £1·20.

b) Write down an algebraic equation to illustrate this.   **1**

c) Find the cost of three peaches and two apricots.   **4**

47 Serena buys hoops and stars to make a bracelet.

Two hoops and five stars cost £125.

Let h pounds be the cost of one hoop and s pounds be the cost of one star.

a) Write down an equation in h and s to illustrate the above information.   **1**

Four hoops and three stars cost £145.

b) Write another equation in h and s to illustrate this information.   **1**

c) Hence calculate the cost of one hoop and the cost of one star.   **4**

MARKS

48 A fun park offers two types of entry ticket: adult and child.

Two adult tickets and three child tickets cost £145.

Three adult tickets and four child tickets cost £205.

How much would four adult and one child tickets cost?

6

49 A shop sells two different types of marbles in bags: red and blue.

A bag containing three red and two blue marbles weighs 66 grams.

Let r be the weight, in grams, of a red marble and b be the weight, in grams, of a blue marble.

a) Write down an equation in r and b to illustrate this information.

1

A different bag contains one red and four blue marbles and weighs 72 grams.

b) Write another equation in r and b to illustrate this information.

1

c) Hence find the weight of a bag containing two red and five blue marbles.

4

≫ HOW TO ANSWER

Change the subject of a formula

Change the subject of the formula $c = d\sqrt{k} + h$ to k.

$$c = d\sqrt{k} + h$$

$$c - h = d\sqrt{k}$$

$$\frac{c-h}{d} = \sqrt{k}$$

$$\left(\frac{c-h}{d}\right)^2 = k$$

$$k = \left(\frac{c-h}{d}\right)^2$$

Top Tip!

Subtract h from both sides.

Divide both sides by d.

Square both sides.

Rewrite with k as subject on left-hand side.

MARKS

50 Change the subject of the formula $d = \dfrac{a^2 + 3b}{c}$ to b.

3

51 Change the subject of the formula $m = \sqrt{5np - t}$ to n.

3

52 $y = \dfrac{3(2w - v)}{7}$

Change the subject of the formula to w.

3

53 $m = R^2 t + 4$

Change the subject of the formula to R.

3

54 Change the subject of the formula $b = 7 + \dfrac{5}{d}$ to d.

3

55 **a)** Change the subject of the formula $z = 2\sqrt{t} + s$ to t.

3

b) Calculate the value of t when $z = 3{\cdot}6$ and $s = 2{\cdot}3$

2

≫ HOW TO ANSWER

Quadratic function: graphs

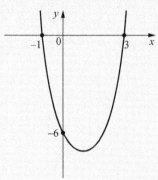

The diagram shows part of the graph of a quadratic function, with equation of the form
$y = k(x - a)(x - b)$

The graph cuts the y-axis at $(0, -6)$.

The graph cuts the x-axis at $(-1, 0)$ and $(3, 0)$.

a)   Write down the values of a and b.

b)   Calculate the value of k.

c)   Find the coordinates of the minimum turning point of the function.

a   Cuts at $x = -1$ and $x = 3$

   giving $a = -1$ and $b = 3$

b $y = k(x + 1)(x - 3)$

   $-6 = k(0 + 1)(0 - 3)$

   $-6 = -3k$

   $k = 2$

c   Using $x = 1$

   $y = 2(1 + 1)(1 - 3) = -8$

   Turning point is at $(1, -8)$

Top Tip!

Zeros of function.

Replace a and b with their values from **a**.

Replace x and y with $(0, -6)$.

Top Tip!

x-coordinate of turning point is $\frac{1}{2}$ way between zeros.

56 The diagram shows part of the graph of a quadratic function, with equation of the form $y = k(x - a)(x - b)$.

The graph cuts the y-axis at $(0, -10)$.

The graph cuts the x-axis at $(-1, 0)$ and $(5, 0)$.

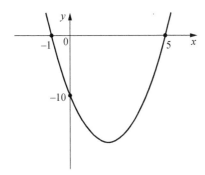

    a) Write down the values of a and b.   **2**

    b) Calculate the value of k.   **2**

    c) Find the coordinates of the minimum turning point.   **2**

57 The diagram shows part of the graph of $y = 5 + 4x - x^2$.

A is the point $(-1, 0)$.

B is the point $(5, 0)$.

    a) State the equation of the axis of symmetry of the graph.   **2**

    b) Hence find the maximum value of $y = 5 + 4x - x^2$.   **2**

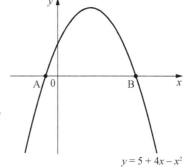

$y = 5 + 4x - x^2$

58 The profit made by a publishing company of a magazine is calculated by the formula $y = 5x(160 - x)$, where y is the profit, in pounds, and x is the selling price, in pence, of the magazine.   **4**

The graph below represents the profit, y, against the selling price, x.

Find the maximum profit the company can make from selling the magazine.

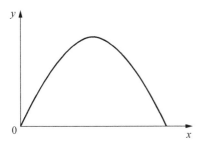

59 Sketch the graph of $y = (x - 4)(x + 6)$.   **3**

On your sketch, show clearly the points of intersection with the x-axis and the y-axis, and the coordinates of the turning point.

60 A graph has equation $y = x^2 + 4x + 5$.

    a) Write $x^2 + 4x + 5$ in the form $(x + a)^2 + b$ and state the values of a and b.   **2**

    b) Hence sketch the graph of $y = x^2 + 4x + 5$, clearly showing the coordinates of the turning point.   **2**

    c) State the equation of the axis of symmetry of the graph.   **1**

≫ HOW TO ANSWER

Quadratic equations: factorising, using the formula and the discriminant

Determine the nature of the roots of the equation $2x^2 - 3x - 1 = 0$.

$2x^2 - 3x - 1$

$a = 2, b = -3, c = -1$

$b^2 - 4ac = (-3)^2 - 4(2)(-1)$

$\qquad = 9 + 8 = 17$

$17 > 0$

Therefore, there are two real, distinct, roots.

Top Tip!

Use the discriminant $b^2 - 4ac$ and then compare with > 0, $= 0$ and < 0.

MARKS

61 Solve the equation $x^2 + x - 6 = 0$. 2

62 Solve the equation $2x^2 + 7x - 15 = 0$. 3

63 Solve the equation $2w^2 - w - 10 = 0$. 3

64 The diagrams show a rectangle and a triangle.

All measurements are in centimetres.

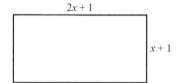 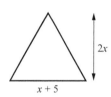

    a) Find an expression for the area of the rectangle. 1

    b) Given that the area of the rectangle is **equal** to the area of the triangle, show that $x^2 - 2x + 1 = 0$. 2

    c) Hence find, algebraically, the length and width of the rectangle. 3

65 Determine the nature of the roots of the function $f(x) = 2x^2 + 4x + 3$. 3

66 Determine the nature of the roots of the function $f(x) = 6x^2 + 5x - 1$. 3

67 Determine the nature of the roots of the function $f(x) = x^2 + 6x + 9$. 3

68 Solve the equation $2x^2 + 5x - 4 = 0$. 3
    Give your answer correct to 1 decimal place.

69 Find the two roots of the equation $2x^2 - 3x - 4 = 0$. 3
    Give your answer correct to 1 decimal place.

70 Solve the equation $x^2 + 2x - 6 = 0$. 4
    Give your answer correct to 2 significant figures.

Geometric skills

≫ HOW TO ANSWER

Arcs and sectors

The area of paper used to make the fan shown is 235 cm².

What is the length of the 'blade' of the fan, marked b?

Give your answer to 1 decimal place.

235 cm² 120° b

$$\text{Area} = \frac{\text{angle}}{360} \times \pi r^2$$

$$235 = \frac{120}{360} \times \pi r^2$$

$$705 = \pi r^2$$

$$224 \cdot 408... = r^2$$

$$r = \sqrt{224 \cdot 408...}$$

$$= 14 \cdot 98$$

Length of blade, b, is 15·0 cm, to 1 d.p.

Top Tip!

Remember the formula for calculating the area of a sector is:

$$\text{Area of sector} = \frac{\text{angle}}{360} \times \pi r^2$$

MARKS

1 The landing area for a discus is a sector of a circle as shown.

The angle at centre O is 35°.

The length of each 'arm' is 80 metres.

a) What is the length of the outer arc?

3

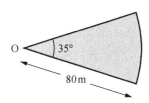

O 35° 80 m

b) What is the area of the sector?

3

2 The diagram shows a sector of a circle, centre C.

3

Angle ACB is 160°, and the radius of the circle is 30 centimetres.

Calculate the length of the arc AB.

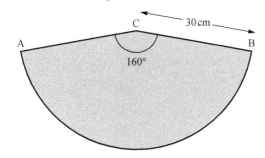

C 30 cm A B 160°

3 The diagram shows a tent made of canvas.

The canvas used is in the shape of a sector of a circle as shown.

O is the centre of the circle.

OA and OB are radii of length 4 metres.

Calculate the area of canvas used.

3

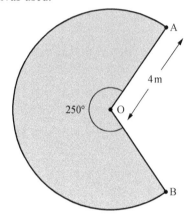

4 The pattern for a skirt consists of part of the sector of a circle, as shown.

Calculate the area of material need to make this skirt.

4

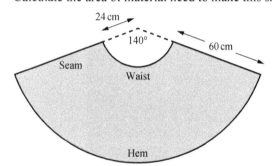

5 A pirate boat on a fairground ride travels along an arc of a circle, centre C.

The boat is attached to C by a metal rod, 7 metres long.

The rod swings from position CA to CB.

The length of arc AB is 8 metres.

Calculate the angle through which the rod swings as it moves from position A to position B.

4

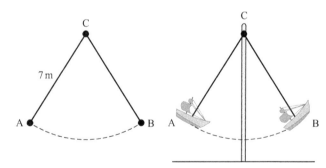

6 A security system sensor covers an area in the shape of a sector of a circle, centre S, as shown in the diagram.

The area covered by the sensor is 250 square metres.

Find the size of the angle at S.

4

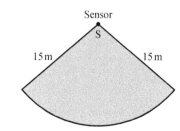

>> HOW TO ANSWER

Volume of standard and composite solids

A mug is in the shape of a cylinder, with diameter 10 cm, and height 14 cm.

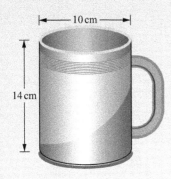

a)   Calculate the volume of the mug.

b)   600 millilitres of tea are poured into the mug.
     Calculate the depth of tea in the mug.

a $V = \pi r^2 h$

    $= \pi \times 5^2 \times 14$

    $= 1099.557...$

    $= 1099.6 \, cm^3$

b $V = \pi r^2 h$

    $600 = \pi \times 5^2 \times h$

    $h = 600 \div 25\pi$

       $= 7.639... \, cm$

The depth of tea in the mug is 7.6 cm.

> **Top Tip!**
>
> Write down formula for volume of cylinder.
>
> Substitute into formula. $d = 10$ so $r = 5$.

7 A cylindrical paperweight with radius 3 centimetres and height 4 centimetres is filled with sand.

   a)   Calculate the volume of sand required to fill the paperweight.

   b)   A second paperweight is a hemisphere that is filled with sand.
        It contains the same volume of sand as the first paperweight.
        Calculate the radius of the hemisphere.

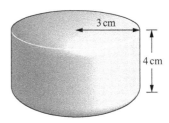

2

3

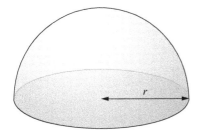

> **Hint!**
>
> The formula for the volume of a hemisphere is $V = \dfrac{2}{3}\pi r^3$.

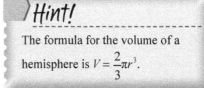

MARKS

8 A child's 'wobbly toy' is in the shape of a hemisphere with a cone on top, as shown in the diagram.

The toy is 10 centimetres wide and 30 centimetres tall.

Calculate the volume of the toy.

Give your answer correct to 2 significant figures.

5

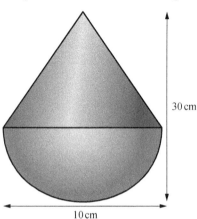

30 cm

10 cm

9 A cylindrical soup can is 15 centimetres high, and has a diameter of 6·5 centimetres.

a) Find the volume of this soup can.

2

b) The height of the can is then reduced to 12 centimetres, but the volume stays the same.

Calculate the diameter of the new can.

Give your answer correct to one decimal place.

3

10 A garden planter is prism-shaped as shown.

It is 3 metres long and has a cross-section made up of a rectangle and semicircle as shown.

Find the volume of the planter.

Give your answer correct to 2 significant figures.

5

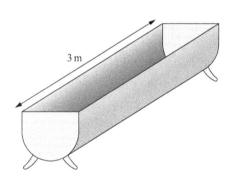

3 m

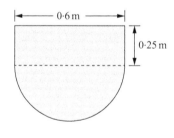

0·6 m

0·25 m

≫ HOW TO ANSWER

Applying Pythagoras' theorem

Dave is making a rectangular picture frame.

The height of the frame is 40 centimetres.

The width of the frame is 25·5 centimetres, as shown.

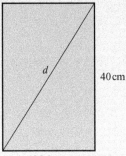

40 cm

25·5 cm

To check that the frame is rectangular, a diagonal, d, is measured.

d is 47·6 centimetres long.

Is the frame rectangular?

Sides: $40^2 + 25·5^2 = 2250·25$

Diagonal: $47·6^2 = 2265·76$

$2250·25 \neq 2265·76$

$a^2 + b^2 \neq c^2$

So, by converse of Pythagoras the frame is not right-angled and, therefore, not rectangular.

Top Tip!

Use Pythagoras' theorem to check that half of the frame forms a right-angled triangle.

A cuboid has dimensions of length 10 centimetres, breadth 4 centimetres, and height 6 centimetres.

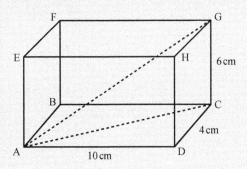

6 cm

4 cm

10 cm

a) Calculate the length of the face diagonal AC.

b) Hence calculate the length of the space diagonal AG.

a $(AC)^2 = 10^2 + 4^2 = 116$
$AC = \sqrt{116} = 10·77\,cm$

b $(AG)^2 = \sqrt{116}^2 + 6^2 = 152$
$AG = \sqrt{152} = 12·33\,cm$

MARKS

11 The cuboid ABCDEFGH has dimensions as shown.

a) Calculate the length of the face diagonal AC. **2**

b) Hence calculate the length of space diagonal AG. **2**

Give your answer correct to 2 significant figures.

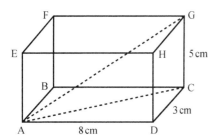

12 Mark wants to store his hockey stick in a locker. **4**

The locker has dimensions as shown.

His hockey stick is 36·5 inches long.

Mark thinks it will fit in the locker from corner P to corner Q.

Is Mark correct?

Justify your answer.

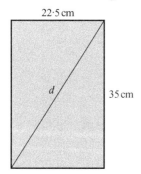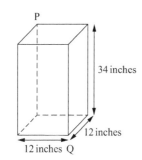

13 A rectangular picture frame is to be made. **4**

It is 35 centimetres high and 22·5 centimetres wide.

To check that the frame is rectangular the diagonal, *d*, is measured.

The diagonal measures 41·4 centimetres.

Is the frame rectangular?

14 The ACME company makes mathematical instruments.

It is making a new size of set square, **which must have a perfect right angle in one corner**.

If the set square has sides of lengths 14·4 centimetres, 10·8 centimetres and 18 centimetres, will it be acceptable?

You must justify your answer.

4

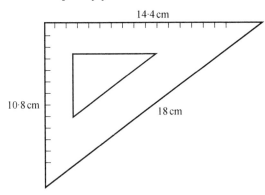

14·4 cm

10·8 cm

18 cm

15 A mirror is in the shape of part of a circle as shown.

The radius of the circle, centre C, is 24 centimetres.

The height of the mirror is 35 centimetres.

Calculate the length of the base of the mirror, shown as AB in the diagram.

4

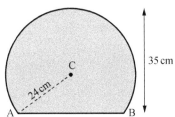

35 cm

C

24 cm

A   B

16 The diagram shows water lying in a length of roof guttering.

The cross-section of the guttering is a semicircle of diameter 12 centimetres.

The water surface is 9 centimetres wide.

Calculate the depth, d, of water in the guttering.

4

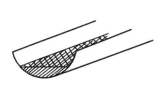 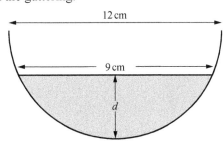

12 cm

9 cm

d

17 The diagram shows the circular cross-section of a tunnel, with a horizontal floor.

In the diagram AB represents the floor, which is 2·4 metres wide.

The radius of the cross-section of the tunnel is 2·5 metres.

Calculate the height of the tunnel.

4

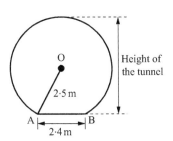 

O

Height of the tunnel

2·5 m

A   B

2·4 m

≫ HOW TO ANSWER

Circles and polygons

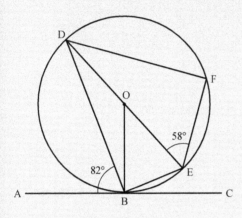

AC is a tangent to the circle, centre O, with point of contact at B.

DE is the diameter of the circle and point F is on the circumference of the circle.

Angle ABD is 82° and angle DEF is 58°.

Calculate the size of angle BDF.

Angle BDF = Angle EDF + Angle BDE

Angle EDF = 90 − 58 = 32°

Angle OBD = 90 − 82 = 8°

Angle BDE = 8°

Angle BDF = 32 + 8 = 40°

Top Tip!

Triangle DEF is an 'angle in a semicircle'.

OB is a radius. A radius meets a tangent at 90°.

OBD is an isosceles triangle, so angle BDE = angle OBD.

MARKS

3

18 AC is a tangent to the circle, centre O, with point of contact at B.

DE is the diameter of the circle and point F is on the circumference of the circle.

Angle ABD is 75° and angle DEF is 54°.

Calculate the size of angle BDF.

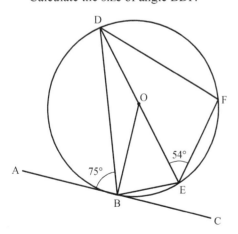

19 The top of a coffee table is in the shape of a regular hexagon.

The three diagonals of the hexagon are shown as dotted lines in the diagram.

Each diagonal is 1 metre long.

Calculate the area of the top of the coffee table.

4

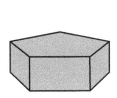 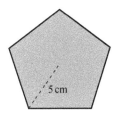

> **Hint!**
> You will need to use trigonometry; use the formula to calculate the area of a triangle.

20 A jewellery box is in the shape of a regular pentagon.

The dotted line is the 'radius' of the pentagon, 5 centimetres long.

Calculate the area of the top of the jewellery box.

4

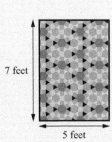 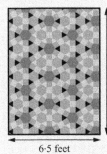

5 cm

≫ HOW TO ANSWER

Similarity

Craig is looking to buy a new rug for his living room.

The two rugs below are mathematically similar.

7 feet

length

5 feet

6·5 feet

Craig is hoping the large rug will be long enough so that the rug's area will be at least 65 square feet.

Does the large rug have the required area?

You must show appropriate working to justify your answer.

For a minimum area of 65 square feet, the length of the large rug must be at least 10 feet (10 × 6·5 = 65).

$$\text{Scale factor} = \frac{\text{new}}{\text{original}} = \frac{6·5}{5} = 1·3$$

Length of larger rug = 7 × 1·3 = 9·1 feet

9·1 < 10 so large rug is not long enough.

> **Top Tip!**
> Work out the scale factor using corresponding sides.

MARKS

21 Coffee is sold in *Regular* cups and *Grande* cups.

The two cups are mathematically similar in shape.

The *Regular* cup is 12 centimetres in height and holds 160 millilitres of coffee.

The *Grande* cup is 18 centimetres in height.

Calculate how many millilitres the *Grande* cup holds.

4

Regular   *Grande*

22 Two perfume bottles are mathematically similar in shape.

The larger bottle is 9 centimetres high and holds 135 millilitres of perfume.

The smaller bottle is 6 centimetres high.

What volume of perfume does the smaller bottle hold?

3

23 Two paintings are mathematically similar in shape.

The cost of each painting is proportional to its area.

The large painting costs £137·50.

Find the cost of the smaller painting.

3

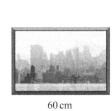 

60 cm   100 cm

24 Calculate the length of AC in this triangle.

3

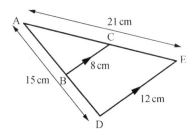

MARKS

4

25 Two tins of paint are mathematically similar.

The smaller tin holds 400 millilitres of paint, and is 10 centimetres high.

The larger tin holds 1000 millilitres of paint.

Find the height of the larger tin.

10 cm

400 ml   1000 ml

>> HOW TO ANSWER

2D and 3D vectors

Two forces acting on an object are represented by vectors **a** and **b**.

$$\mathbf{a} = \begin{pmatrix} 2 \\ -1 \\ -1 \end{pmatrix} \qquad \mathbf{b} = \begin{pmatrix} 6 \\ -1 \\ 3 \end{pmatrix}$$

Calculate $|\mathbf{a} + \mathbf{b}|$, the magnitude of the resultant force.

Express your answer as a surd in its simplest form.

$$\mathbf{a} + \mathbf{b} = \begin{pmatrix} 2 \\ -1 \\ -1 \end{pmatrix} + \begin{pmatrix} 6 \\ -1 \\ 3 \end{pmatrix} = \begin{pmatrix} 8 \\ -2 \\ 2 \end{pmatrix}$$

$$|\mathbf{a} + \mathbf{b}|^2 = 8^2 + (-2)^2 + 2^2 = 72$$

$$|\mathbf{a} + \mathbf{b}| = \sqrt{72} = 6\sqrt{2}$$

> **Top Tip!**
>
> Use the formula $|\mathbf{a}|^2 = x^2 + y^2 + z^2$ to work out the magnitude.
>
> Write your answer as a surd in its simplest form.

MARKS

26 Point A is (4, −2, 7).

$$\overrightarrow{AB} \text{ is } \begin{pmatrix} 3 \\ 5 \\ -2 \end{pmatrix}$$

Write down the coordinates of point B.

2

27 A cuboid is drawn on a coordinate diagram as shown.

The coordinates of E are (4, 3, 2).

a) Write down the coordinates of F.   **1**

b) Write down the coordinates of G.   **1**

c) Calculate the shortest distance between points C and D.   **2**

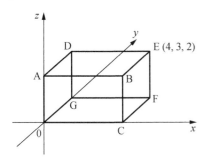

28 ABCDEF is a regular hexagon with centre O.

$\overrightarrow{OA} = a$ and $\overrightarrow{AB} = b$

Find an expression, in terms of a and b, for $\overrightarrow{EC}$

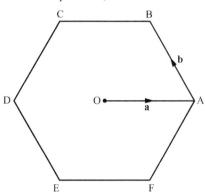

29 The vectors **p** and **q** are shown on the diagram below.

Find the resultant vector **p** + **q**.

Express your answer in component form.

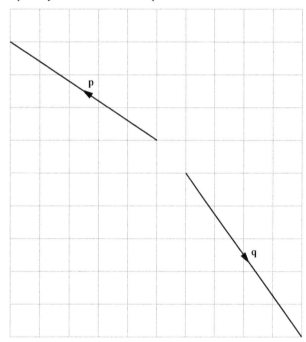

30 In the diagram, ABCDEF is a regular hexagon with centre, M.

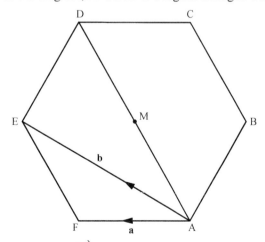

a) Express $\overrightarrow{FE}$ in terms of **a** and **b**.

b) Express $\overrightarrow{AD}$ in terms of **a** and **b**.

Trigonometric skills

›› HOW TO ANSWER

Graphs of trigonometric functions

Part of the graph of $y = a\cos x° + b$ is shown.

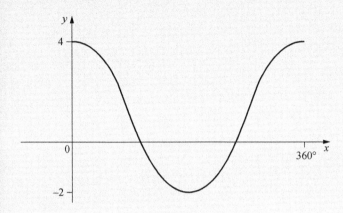

a) Explain how you can tell from the graph that $a = 3$ and $b = 1$.

b) Calculate the x-coordinates of where the graph cuts the x-axis.

a) a is the amplitude. It is half the distance from maximum to minimum.

Max to min is 6, and $\dfrac{1}{2}$ of $6 = 3$

So $a = 3$

b is how far up or down the graph has moved.

$3\cos x°$ goes from a minimum of -3 to a maximum of 3.

This graph has moved up 1 unit, giving $b = 1$.

b) $3\cos x° + 1 = 0$

$\cos x° = -\dfrac{1}{3}$

$x = \cos^{-1}\left(\dfrac{1}{3}\right)$

$\quad = 180° - 70{\cdot}5°, 180° + 70{\cdot}5°$

$\quad = 109{\cdot}5°, 250{\cdot}5°$

Top Tip!

The graph cuts the x-axis when $y = 0$.

Use a CAST diagram.

✓ S	A
✓ T	C

MARKS

1 Part of the graph of $y = a\cos x° + b$ is shown.

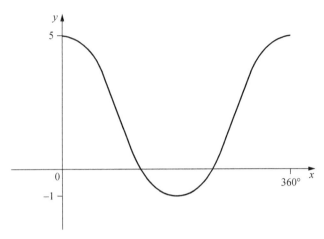

    a)   Explain how you can tell from the graph that $a = 3$ and $b = 2$.   **2**

    b)   Calculate the x-coordinates of where the graph cuts the x-axis.   **4**

2 Part of the graph of $y = a\sin bx°$ is shown.   **2**

Write down the values of a and b.

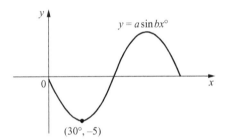

3 The diagram shows part of the graph of $y = \sin x°$.   **3**

The line $y = 0·3$ is drawn and cuts the graph of $y = \sin x$ at A and B.

Find the x-coordinates of A and B.

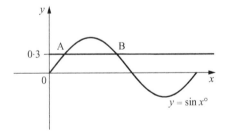

4 Part of the graph of $y = \cos bx° + c$ is shown.   **2**

Write down the values of b and c.

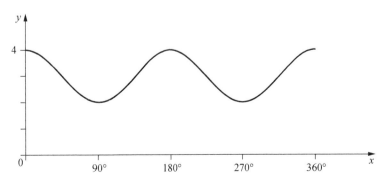

›› HOW TO ANSWER

Trig equations and identities

Solve the equation $11\cos x° - 2 = 3$, for $0 \leq x° \leq 360°$.

$11\cos x° - 2 = 3$

$\quad 11\cos x° = 5$

$\quad \cos x° = \dfrac{5}{11}$

$x = \cos^{-1}\left(\dfrac{5}{11}\right)$

$\quad = 63°, 360° - 63°$

$\quad = 63°, 297°$

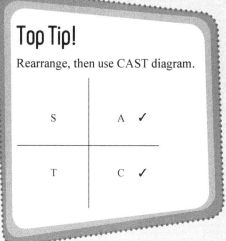

Top Tip!

Rearrange, then use CAST diagram.

S	A ✓
T	C ✓

MARKS

5 Solve the equation $7\sin x° + 2 = 0$, for $0 \leq x° \leq 360°$.   **3**

6 Solve the equation $5\tan x° + 4 = 0$, for $0 \leq x° \leq 360°$.   **3**

7 Solve, algebraically, the equation $4\cos x° + 1 = -2$, for $0 \leq x° \leq 360°$.   **3**

8 On a certain day the depth of water, **D metres**, in a harbour, **t hours after midnight**, is given by the formula   **3**
$D = 12 + 5\sin(30t°)$.

Calculate the depth of water in the harbour at 1 p.m.

9 Simplify $\cos x° \tan x°$.   **2**

10 Show that $\sin x° \cos^2 x° + \sin^3 x° = \sin x°$.   **2**

11 Show that $\dfrac{\sin x°}{\tan x°} = \cos x°$.   **2**

>> HOW TO ANSWER

Area of a triangle using trigonometry

Calculate the area of this triangle.

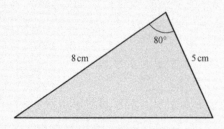

$$\text{Area} = \frac{1}{2}ab\sin C$$

$$= \frac{1}{2} \times 8 \times 5 \sin 80°$$

$$= 19{\cdot}7\,cm^2$$

Top Tip!

The triangle has two sides and an enclosed angle. Find the formula on the formulae list.

MARKS

12 A farmer builds a sheep-pen using two lengths of fencing and an existing wall, as shown in the diagram.

The two lengths of fencing are 14 metres and 17 metres long.

Calculate the area of the sheep-pen when the angle between the fences is 70°.

3

13 In triangle PQR
- QR = 6 centimetres
- angle PQR = 30°
- the area enclosed is 21 cm².

Calculate the length of PQ.

3

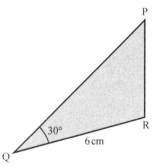

14 A paving slab is in the shape of a rhombus, with side 50 centimetres.

The angle at one of the vertices is 100°.

Calculate the area of one paving slab.

4

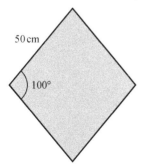

➤➤ HOW TO ANSWER

Sine and cosine rules

A flagpole is attached to a wall and is supported by a wire PQ as shown in the diagram.

PQ is 3·5 metres in length and makes an angle of 55° with the vertical wall.

PR is 4·5 metres in length.

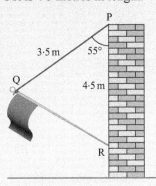

Calculate the length of the flagpole.

$a^2 = b^2 + c^2 - 2bc \cos A$

$p^2 = r^2 + q^2 - 2rq \cos P$

$\quad = 3\cdot5^2 + 4\cdot5^2 - 2(3\cdot5)(4\cdot5)\cos 55°$

$\quad = 14\cdot432$

$p = \sqrt{14.32}$

$\quad = 3\cdot799$ metres

The length of the flagpole is 3·8 metres.

Top Tip!

You are given side, angle, side, which suggests the cosine rule.

Write down the cosine rule from the formulae list.

Rewrite the formula using information in the question, then substitute and calculate.

---

 15 In triangle ABC, calculate the length of AB.　　　　　　　**3**

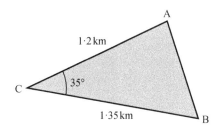

 16 A TV signal is sent from a transmitter, T, via a satellite, S, to a village, V, as shown in the diagram.　　**6**

The village is 500 kilometres from the transmitter.

The signal is sent out at an angle of 40°.

It is received at an angle of 35°.

Calculate the height of the satellite, S, above the ground.

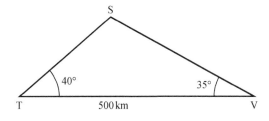

17 The diagram shows a tower.

At A the angle of elevation to the top of the tower is 43°.

At B the angle of elevation to the top of the tower is 74°.

The distance AB is 10 metres.

Calculate the height of the tower.

6

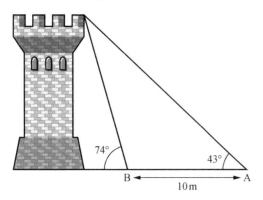

18 In triangle ABC

- AB = 4 centimetres
- AC = 5 centimetres
- BC = 6 centimetres.

Show that $\cos A = \dfrac{1}{8}$

3

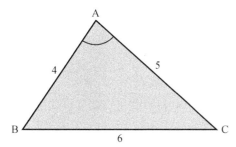

19 As part of his training schedule, Mike runs around a triangular circuit, PQR, as shown.

How many **complete** circuits must Mike run to cover **at least** 1000 metres?

4

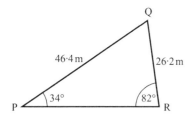

20 The end wall of a house is in the shape of a rectangle and a triangle as shown in the diagram.

One part of the roof is inclined at 25° to the horizontal.

The other is inclined at 41° to the horizontal.

The width of the house is 13·1 metres.

Calculate the length of the longer sloping edge of the roof.

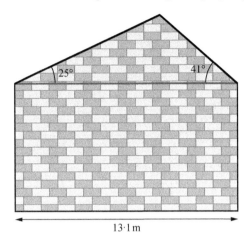

13·1 m

21 The diagram shows part of a golf course.

The distance between holes A and B is 410 metres.

The distance between holes A and C is 520 metres.

Angle BAC is 55°.

Calculate the distance between holes B and C.

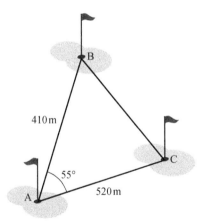

⟫ HOW TO ANSWER

Using bearings with trigonometry

An aeroplane flies from its base, B, on a bearing of 040° for 300 kilometres.

It then changes direction and flies on a bearing of 150° for a further 550 kilometres.

The plane then returns directly to base.

Calculate the distance of the plane's last leg of its journey back to base.

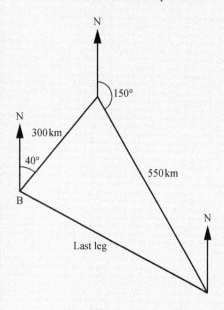

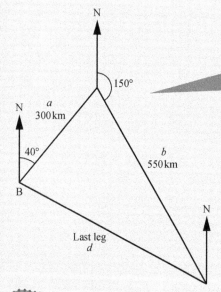

Top Tip!

Find this angle first. Then use cosine rule (SAS).

Top Tip!

Remember alternate angles.

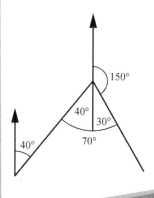

Top Tip!

Check the size of your answer.

Does it look reasonable?

Angle is 70°.

$d^2 = a^2 + b^2 - 2ab\cos 70°$

$= 300^2 + 550^2 - 2(300)(550)\cos 70°$

$= 279633$

$d = \sqrt{279633}$

$= 528 \cdot 8$ kilometres

22 An aeroplane flies from its base, B, on a bearing of 045° for 250 kilometres.

It then changes direction and flies on a bearing of 138° for 470 kilometres.

It then flies directly back to base.

Calculate the distance of the plane's last leg of its journey, back to base.

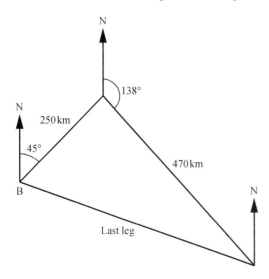

23 Two yachts leave from harbour H.

Yacht A sails on a bearing of 075° for 30 kilometres and stops.

Yacht B sails on a bearing of 142° for 50 kilometres and stops.

How far apart are the two yachts, when they have stopped?

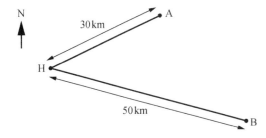

24 Two boats leave port P together.

Boat D sails on a course of 062° at a speed of 15 miles per hour.

Boat E sails on a course of 123° at a speed of 17 miles per hour.

After 45 minutes, boat D receives a distress call from boat E, asking for help as soon as possible.

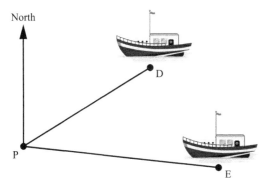

a) How far does boat D have to travel to reach boat E?

b) On what bearing should boat D travel to reach boat E?

MARKS

25 Part of an orienteering course has three checkpoints P, Q and R.

Q is on a bearing of 030° and is 8 kilometres from P.

R is on a bearing of 155° from Q and on a bearing of 105° from P.

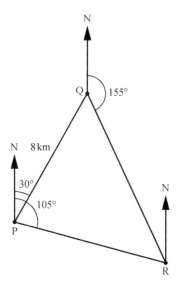

a) Explain why angle PQR = 55°.

2

b) Calculate the distance between points Q and R.

4

26 The diagram shows a helicopter base, H, and two fishing vessels, F and G.

4

From the helicopter base, fishing vessel F is 40 kilometres away on a bearing of 042°.

From the helicopter base, fishing vessel G is 15 kilometres away on a bearing of 155°.

Calculate the distance between the two fishing vessels, F and G.

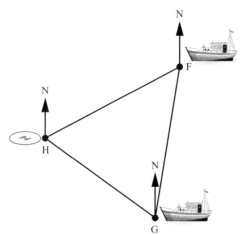

MARKS

27 A group of trekkers take a helicopter from Kathmandu, K, to Pokhara, P, in Nepal, and then onto Annapurna Base Camp, A.

They then fly directly back to Kathmandu.

Pokhara is 90 kilometres from Kathmandu on a bearing of 280°.

Annapurna Base Camp is 35 kilometres from Pokhara on a bearing of 032°.

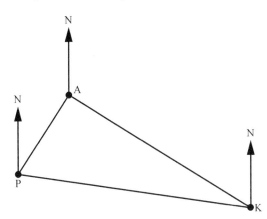

a) What distance must the helicopter fly to return from Annapurna Base Camp to Kathmandu?   **4**

b) On what bearing must the helicopter fly to go directly from Annapurna Base Camp to Kathmandu?   **5**

Statistical and numerical skills

>> HOW TO ANSWER

Surds

Simplify $\sqrt{75} + 4\sqrt{3}$.

$\sqrt{75} + 4\sqrt{3} = \sqrt{(25 \times 3)} + 4\sqrt{3}$

$= 5\sqrt{3} + 4\sqrt{3}$

$= 9\sqrt{3}$

Express $\dfrac{3}{\sqrt{5}}$ as a fraction with a rational denominator.

$\dfrac{3}{\sqrt{5}} = \dfrac{3}{\sqrt{5}} \times \dfrac{\sqrt{5}}{\sqrt{5}}$

$= \dfrac{3\sqrt{5}}{5}$

Top Tip!

Multiply top and bottom by root 5 to rationalise denominator.

MARKS

1 Simplify $\sqrt{48} - 2\sqrt{3}$.   **2**

2 Express $\sqrt{72} + \sqrt{2} - \sqrt{18}$ as a surd in its simplest form.   **3**

3 Express $\sqrt{18} + \sqrt{50}$ as a surd in its simplest form.   **3**

4 Multiply out the brackets $\sqrt{2}\left(\sqrt{10} - \sqrt{2}\right)$.   **3**
Express your answer as a surd in its simplest form.

5 Express $\dfrac{4}{\sqrt{3}}$ as a fraction with a rational denominator.   **2**

6 Simplify $\dfrac{13}{\sqrt{24}}$.   **3**
Express your answer as a fraction with a rational denominator.

≫ HOW TO ANSWER

Indices

Simplify $27^{\frac{2}{3}}$.

$27^{\frac{2}{3}} = \sqrt[3]{(27)^2}$

$\qquad = 3^2$

$\qquad = 9$

Simplify $k^2(k^{-5} + 3)$.

$k^2(k^{-5} + 3) = k^{2 + -5} + 3k^2$

$\qquad\qquad = k^{-3} + 3k^2$

MARKS

7   Evaluate $8^{\frac{2}{3}}$. **2**

8   Evaluate $32^{\frac{3}{5}}$. **2**

9   Simplify $a^{\frac{1}{2}}(a^{\frac{1}{2}} + a^{-\frac{1}{2}})$. **3**

10   Express $y^3 \times \dfrac{y^2}{y^{-2}}$ in its simplest form. **3**

11   Expand the brackets and simplify $t^{\frac{1}{2}}\left(t^{\frac{3}{2}} + \dfrac{1}{t}\right)$. **2**

12   Evaluate $3^0 + 4^{-1}$. **2**

13   $E = mc^2$ **3**

Find E, when $m = 4 \cdot 2 \times 10^{-2}$ and $c = 3 \times 10^8$.

14   The orbit of a planet around a star is circular. **3**

The radius of the orbit is $5 \cdot 78 \times 10^7$ kilometres.

Calculate the circumference of the orbit.

Give your answer in scientific notation.

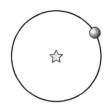

❯❯ HOW TO ANSWER

Percentages

Frank invests £3500 in a high interest account at a rate of 4·2% per annum.

If he does not touch the money in the bank, how much interest will he have gained after 3 years?

Top Tip!

This is a compound percentage question.

Give your answer to the nearest penny.

Total amount $= 3500 \times 1{\cdot}042^3$

$= £3959{\cdot}781$

$= £3959{\cdot}78$ to nearest penny

Interest $= £3959{\cdot}78 - 3500$

$= £459{\cdot}78$

Top Tip!

$100\% + 4.2\% = 104.2\% = 1.042$

Top Tip!

This is a 'reverse percentage' question.

A swimming club's membership increased by 17% in one year.
It now has 351 members.
How many members did it have the previous year?

Top Tip!

$100\% + 17\% = 117\%$
Work out the number of members represented by 1%.
Multiply by 100 to find 100%.

Percentage	Membership
117	351
1	$351 \div 117 = 3$
100	$3 \times 100 = 300$ members

MARKS

15 Dawn invests £5500 in a bank account at 3·8% interest per annum.
If she does not touch the money in the bank, how much interest will she have gained after four years?
Give your answer to the nearest penny.　　4

16 A recycling centre recycles 36 000 tonnes of waste per year.
It aims to increase the amount of waste recycled by 7% per year.
How much waste does the centre expect to recycle in three years?
Give your answer to 3 significant figures.　　4

17 Stacey buys a car for £12 500.
It depreciates at a rate of 11·3% per year.
What will the car be worth after four years?　　3

18 A patient is given 200 milligrams of a drug at 2 p.m.
The amount of drug in the bloodstream decreases by 15% per hour.
How many milligrams of the drug will be in the patient's bloodstream at 7 p.m?　　3

19 Yoghurt is on special offer.

Each tub on special offer contains 15% more than the standard tub.

A tub on special offer contains 345 milligrams of yoghurt.

How much yoghurt does the standard tub contain?

20 Joanne bought a bicycle for £336.

This price included VAT at 20%.

Calculate the price of the bicycle without VAT.

21 Patricia had her jewellery valued at £2750.

This was an increase of 12·5% on her previous valuation.

What was the previous valuation of Patricia's jewellery?

Give your answer correct to 3 significant figures.

22 An antique vase has increased in value by 14% since it was bought.

It is now worth £3620.

What was it worth when it was bought?

Give your answer correct to 3 significant figures.

23 Anwar bought a painting at an auction.

Unfortunately the painting depreciated in value by 8% and it is now worth £3215.

How much was the painting worth when Anwar bought it?

Give your answer to the nearest pound.

24 Saira bought a new car last year.

The car depreciated by 23%. It is now worth £9525.

How much was the car worth when Saira bought it?

Give your answer correct to 3 significant figures.

3

3

4

4

4

4

❯❯ HOW TO ANSWER

Fractions and mixed numbers

Evaluate $34 \cdot 6 - 0 \cdot 7 \times 40$.

$34 \cdot 6 - 0 \cdot 7 \times 40 = 34 \cdot 6 - 28$

$\qquad\qquad\qquad\quad = 6 \cdot 6$

Top Tip!

Remember **BODMAS**:

Brackets

Of

Divide and Multiply

Add and Subtract

MARKS

25 Evaluate $5 \cdot 03 + 2 \cdot 81 \times 20$.　　　　　　　　　　　**2**

26 Evaluate $56 \cdot 4 - 1 \cdot 23 \times 30$.　　　　　　　　　　　**2**

27 Evaluate $1\frac{2}{3} + 4\frac{3}{4}$.　　　　　　　　　　　　　　**2**

28 Evaluate $4\frac{1}{6} + \frac{5}{6}$ of $2\frac{3}{5}$.　　　　　　　　　　**3**

29 Evaluate $7 \cdot 21 - (7 \cdot 16 - 2 \cdot 04)$.　　　　　　　　**2**

30 Evaluate $\frac{2}{7}\left(1\frac{3}{4} + \frac{5}{8}\right)$.　　　　　　　　　　　　　**2**

≫ HOW TO ANSWER

Standard deviation and semi-interquartile range

Kayleigh found out the price of a pint of milk in six local shops.

The prices, in pence, were:

59, 54, 51, 62, 57, 53

a) Find the mean price of a pint of milk in these shops.

b) Calculate the standard deviation for these prices.

c) Kayleigh also found out the prices at some supermarkets. She found the mean price to be 54 pence and the standard deviation to be 3·7 pence.

Make two valid comparisons between the prices in the local shops and in the supermarkets.

a $\text{Mean} = \dfrac{\text{total}}{\text{number of items}}$

$= \dfrac{336}{6} = 56$ pence

b Standard deviation

Top Tip!

Check this column should total 0

x	$\bar{x}$	$x - \bar{x}$	$(x - \bar{x})^2$
59	56	3	9
54	56	−2	4
51	56	−5	25
62	56	6	36
57	56	1	1
53	56	−3	9
336		0	84

$\text{s.d.} = \sqrt{\dfrac{\Sigma(x - \bar{x})^2}{n - 1}}$

$= \sqrt{\left(\dfrac{84}{5}\right)}$

$= 4·1$ pence

c On average the price of milk in supermarkets was lower than in local shops.

The prices in the supermarkets were more consistent than in local shops.

MARKS

 31 A general knowledge quiz was marked out of 50.

The results for a group of people were as follows:

30, 25, 38, 45, 36, 40, 28, 43, 39

Calculate the mean and standard deviation of these scores.

3

 32 Zishan noted these prices of a loaf of bread in five local shops:

£1·22, £1·40, £1·28, £1·25, £1·35

a) Calculate the mean price.

1

b) Calculate the standard deviation of the prices.

2

33 The times, in seconds, taken by some boys to swim one length of a pool were as follows:

28·3, 25·6, 29·4, 26·5, 32·7, 27·3, 26·2, 24·8

    a) Calculate the mean and standard deviation for this data.   **3**

A group of girls also swam one length of the pool. Their mean time was 31·5 seconds and the standard deviation was 1·76 seconds.

    b) Make two valid statements comparing the times for the boys and the girls.   **2**

34 The weights, in kilograms, of seven Sixth Year students were:

42, 58, 53, 62, 48, 51, 71

    a) Calculate the mean weight for this sample.   **1**

    b) Calculate the standard deviation for this sample.   **3**

The mean weight of all the Sixth Year students was 62 kg.

The standard deviation was 8·2 kg.

    c) Make two valid statements comparing the group of seven students with the whole year group.   **2**

35 Police recorded the speeds, in miles per hour, of cars passing a checkpoint.

The results were as follows:

47, 53, 52, 55, 60, 48, 57, 57, 49, 56

Calculate the semi-interquartile range.   **3**

> *Hint!*
> ------------------------------------
> Order the data, then work out Q_1 and Q_3.
> The semi-interquartile range is half of the
> interquartile range, $Q_3 - Q_1$.

≫ HOW TO ANSWER

Scattergraphs

The scattergraph shows the relationship between the age, A years, and value, V (£000s), of some cars in a showroom.

A line of best fit has been drawn.

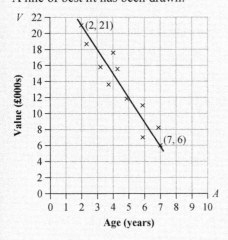

a) Find the equation of the line of best fit in terms of V and A.

b) Use the equation of the line of best fit to estimate the value of a car which is eight years old.

a $$m = \frac{y_2 - y_1}{x_2 - x_1}$$

$$= \frac{21 - 6}{2 - 7}$$

$$= -3$$

$$y - 6 = -3(x - 7)$$

$$y = -3x + 27$$

$$V = -3A + 27$$

b $V = -3A + 27$

$$= -3(8) + 27 = 3$$

Value of 8-year-old car is £3000.

Top Tip!

Use the formula $y - b = m(x - a)$ and substitute values.
Use one of the points on the line, (7, 6).

Rewrite in terms of V and A.

36 The scattergraph shows the ages, *A* years, of some young people and the distance, *M* metres, they jumped in a long-jump competition.

A line of best fit has been drawn.

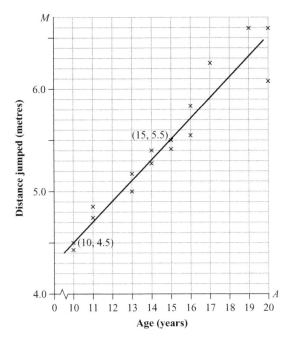

a) Find the equation, in terms of *M* and *A*, of this line of best fit. **4**

b) Use your equation to estimate the distance a nine-year old would jump. **1**

37 Jacob buys apples from the market each week.

He keeps a record of how many apples, *A*, he buys, and the cost, *C* pence.

He plots this information on a graph and draws in a line of best fit.

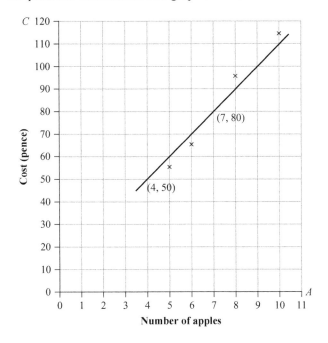

a) Find the equation of this line of best fit. **4**

b) Use the equation to estimate the cost if Jacob buys two apples. **1**

Algebraic skills

Expanding brackets and simplifying

Question	Expected answer	Mark	Commentary	Demand
1	$9x^2 + 6x - 15x - 10$ ✓ $= 9x^2 - 9x - 10$ ✓	2	Start to multiply. Collect like terms.	C
2	$6x^2 - 4x + 15x - 10$ ✓ $= 6x^2 + 11x - 10$ ✓	2	Start to multiply. Collect like terms.	C
3	$12k^2 - 3ky + 20ky - 5y^2$ ✓ $= 12k^2 + 17ky - 5y^2$ ✓	2	Start to multiply. Collect like terms.	C
4	$12x - 4$ ✓ $\ldots - 10x - 15$ ✓ $= 2x - 19$ ✓	3	Expand first bracket. Expand second bracket. Collect like terms.	C
5	$9x^2 - 15x - 15x + 25$ ✓ $= 9x^2 - 30x + 25$ ✓	2	Set up as pair of brackets or evidence of 'square the first …'	C
6	$9x^2 + 12x + 4$ ✓ $\ldots + 15x - 10$ ✓ $= 9x^2 + 27x - 6$ ✓	3	First bracket. Second bracket. Simplify.	C
7	$12x^2 - 5x - 2$ ✓ $\ldots + 6x^2 + 2$ ✓ $= 18x^2 - 5x$ ✓	3	First bracket. Second bracket. Simplify.	C
8	$4x^3 + 6x^2 + 2x$ ✓ $\ldots + 6x^2 + 9x + 3$ ✓ $= 4x^3 + 12x^2 + 11x + 3$ ✓	3	Multiply by $2x$. Multiply by 3. Collect like terms.	C
9	$12x^3 + 15x^2 - 9x$ ✓ $\ldots - 8x^2 - 10x + 6$ ✓ $= 12x^3 + 7x^2 - 19x + 6$ ✓	3	Multiply by first term. Multiply by second term. Simplify.	C
10	$12x^3 - 6x^2 + 15x$ ✓ $\ldots -8x^2 + 4x - 10$ ✓ $= 12x^3 - 14x^2 + 19x - 10$ ✓	3	Multiply by first term. Multiply by second term. Simplify.	C

Factorising and completing the square

Question	Expected answer	Mark	Commentary	Demand
11	$3x(x-6)$ ✔✔	2	Take out common factor. Factorise bracket.	C
12	$3x(2x-3)$ ✔✔	2	Take out common factor. Factorise bracket.	C
13	$(x-8)(x+8)$ ✔	1	Difference of two squares.	C
14	$(3a-2b)(3a+2b)$ ✔✔	2	For $3a$ and $2b$. Difference of two squares.	C
15	$(x+5)(x+3)$ ✔✔	2	One mark for each bracket.	C
16	$(x-4)(x+1)$ ✔✔	2	One mark for each bracket.	C
17	$(3x+1)(x-4)$ ✔✔	2	One mark for each bracket.	>C
18	$(3x+2)(2x-5)$ ✔✔	2	One mark for each bracket.	>C
19	$(x+4)^2 + 12 - 16$ ✔✔ $= (x+4)^2 - 4$ ✔	3	One mark for $(x+4)$. One mark for -16. One mark for final answer.	C
20	$(x-2)^2 + 1 - 4$ ✔✔ $= (x-2)^2 - 3$ ✔	3	One mark for $(x-2)$. One mark for -4. One mark for final answer.	C

Algebraic fractions

Question	Expected answer	Mark	Commentary	Demand
21	$\dfrac{4}{12x} - \dfrac{3}{12x}$ ✔ $= \dfrac{1}{12x}$ ✔	2	Common denominator.	C
22	$\dfrac{4x}{x^2} - \dfrac{(3-x)}{x^2}$ ✔ $= \dfrac{4x-(3-x)}{x^2}$ ✔ $= \dfrac{5x-3}{x^2}$ ✔	3	Multiply first fraction by x. Subtract numerators. Simplify.	>C
23	$\dfrac{5(x-2)}{x(x-2)} + \dfrac{2x}{x(x-2)}$ ✔ $= \dfrac{5x-10}{x(x-2)} + \dfrac{2x}{x(x-2)}$ ✔ $= \dfrac{7x-10}{x(x-2)}$ ✔	3	Common denominator. Add numerators. Simplify.	C
24	a) $(2a-b)(2a+b)$ ✔ b) $\dfrac{(2a-b)(2a+b)}{4(2a-b)}$ ✔ $= \dfrac{(2a+b)}{4}$ ✔	3	Difference of two squares. Substitute into numerator and factorise denominator. Cancel.	C

Question	Expected answer	Mark	Commentary	Demand
25	**a)** $(x+3)(x-2)$ ✓ **b)** $\dfrac{(x+3)(x-2)}{(x+3)^2}$ ✓ $= \dfrac{(x-2)}{(x+3)}$ ✓	3	Factorise quadratic. Substitute into numerator. Cancel.	C
26	$\dfrac{(x+6)(x+2)}{(x+2)}$ ✓✓ $= x+6$ ✓	3	Higher demand as no 'lead in'.	>C
27	$\dfrac{(x-2)}{3} \times \dfrac{3}{(x-2)(x+2)}$ ✓✓ $= \dfrac{1}{(x+2)}$ ✓	3	Invert and multiply. Difference of two squares. Cancel.	>C
28	$3(x-4) - 2(x+1) = 6$ ✓ $x - 14 = 6$ ✓ $x = 20$ ✓	3	Multiply by 6 (or equivalent). Expand and simplify. Solve.	>C
29	$3(x-3) + 2(2x-1) = 24$ ✓ $7x - 11 = 24$ ✓ $7x = 35$ ✓ $x = 5$ ✓	4	Multiply by 6 (or equivalent). Expand and simplify. Solve.	>C
30	$4(x-2) - 6x = 3$ ✓ $4x - 8 - 6x = 3$ ✓ $-2x = 11$ ✓ $x = -\dfrac{11}{2}$ ✓	4	Multiply by 12. Expand and simplify. Solve.	>C

Find/interpret equation of a straight line

Question	Expected answer	Mark	Commentary	Demand
31	$c = 5$ ✓ $m = 10$ ✓ $y = 10x + 5$ ✓	3	Find y-intercept. Calculate gradient. Write full equation.	C
32	$c = 5$ ✓ $m = \dfrac{35}{60} = \dfrac{7}{12}$ ✓ $V = \dfrac{7}{12}t + 5$ ✓	3	Find y-intercept. Calculate gradient. Write full equation using correct letters (V for volume, t for time).	C
33	**a)** $c = 11,\ m = \dfrac{70}{90} = \dfrac{7}{9}$ ✓✓ $g = \dfrac{7}{9}h + 11$ ✓ **b)** $g = \dfrac{7}{9}(54) + 11$ $= 53$ marks ✓	4	Find y-intercept. Find gradient. Substitute into formula. Substitute 54 into equation of the line.	C

Question	Expected answer	Mark	Commentary	Demand
14	Area of $\frac{1}{2}$ slab $= \frac{1}{2}(50)(50)\sin 100$ $= 1231\,\text{cm}^2$ ✓ ✓ Area of whole slab $= 2 \times 1231$ $= 2462\,\text{cm}^2$ ✓ ✓	4	Substitute in area formula (for 1/2 slab). Calculate. Double the calculated area for the area of the whole slab.	>C

Sine and cosine rules

Question	Expected answer	Mark	Commentary	Demand
15	$AB^2 = AC^2 + BC^2 - 2\,AC \cdot BC \cdot \cos C$ ✓ $AB^2 = 1{\cdot}2^2 + 1{\cdot}35^2 - 2 \times 1{\cdot}2 \times 1{\cdot}35 \times \cos 35$ ✓ $AB = 0{\cdot}78\,\text{km}$ ✓	3	State cosine rule. Substitute values. Calculate.	C
16	Angle S $= 105°$ ✓ $\dfrac{a}{\sin A} = \dfrac{b}{\sin B}$ ✓ $\dfrac{500}{\sin 105} = \dfrac{SV}{\sin 40}$ ✓ $SV = \dfrac{500 \sin 40}{\sin 105}$ $= 332{\cdot}7\,\text{m}$ ✓ $\sin 35 = \dfrac{\text{height}}{332{\cdot}7}$ ✓ height $= 332{\cdot}7 \sin 35$ $= 190{\cdot}8\,\text{km}$ ✓	6	Find SV (or TS). Use sine rule to calculate distance SV. Use sine ratio to calculate height. Use right-angled trig to calculate height.	>C
17	Angle B $= 106°$ so upper angle of triangle $= 31°$ ✓ $\dfrac{a}{\sin 43} = \dfrac{10}{\sin 31}$ ✓ $a = \dfrac{10 \sin 43}{\sin 31}$ ✓ $= 13{\cdot}2\,\text{metres}$ ✓ $\sin 74 = \dfrac{\text{height}}{13{\cdot}2}$ ✓ height $= 13{\cdot}2 \sin 74$ $= 12{\cdot}7\,\text{metres}$ ✓	6	Use the sine rule to calculate distance a. Use right-angled trig to calculate height.	>C
18	$\cos A = \dfrac{(b^2 + c^2 - a^2)}{2bc}$ ✓ $= \dfrac{(4^2 + 5^2 - 6^2)}{2 \times 4 \times 5}$ ✓ $= \dfrac{5}{40}$ $= \dfrac{1}{8} = \text{RHS}$ ✓	3	State cosine rule. Substitute values. State proof.	C

Question	Expected answer	Mark	Commentary	Demand
19	Angle PQR = 64° ✓ Method 1 (Sine Rule) $\dfrac{q}{\sin 64°} = \dfrac{26\cdot2}{\sin 34°}$ $q = 26\cdot2\,\dfrac{\sin 64°}{\sin 34°}$ $= 42\cdot1\text{ metres }$ ✓ Perimeter = 114·7 metres $1000 \div 114\cdot7 = 8.72$ ✓ Must complete 9 circuits ✓ Method 2 (Cosine rule) $q^2 = 46.4^2 + 26.2^2 - 2(46.4)(26.2)\cos 64°$ $= 1773.56$ $q = 42.1$ metres ✓ then as before	4	Find angle PQR. Use sin or cos rule to find side q. Divide 1000 by perimeter. Round up.	C
20	Angle at top of roof = 114° ✓ $\dfrac{13\cdot1}{\sin 114} = \dfrac{\text{long slope}}{\sin 41}$ ✓ Long slope $= \dfrac{13\cdot1 \sin 41}{\sin 114}$ ✓ $= 9.4\,\text{m}$ ✓	4	Find angle at top of roof. Use Sine Rule. Substitute values and calculate.	C
21	cos rule (SAS) ✓ $BC^2 = 520^2 + 410^2 - 2(520)(410)\cos 55$ ✓ $= 193\,927$ $BC = 440\,\text{m}$ ✓	3	Use cosine rule. Substitute in rule. Calculate.	C

Using bearings with trigonometry

Question	Expected answer	Mark	Commentary	Demand
22	87° ✓ $D^2 = 250^2 + 470^2 - 2(250)(470)\cos 87$ ✓ $= 271\,101$ ✓ $D = 520\cdot7\,(521)\,\text{km}$ ✓	4	Find required angle. Use cosine rule.	>C
23	67° ✓ $D^2 = 30^2 + 50^2 - 2(30)(50)\cos 67$ ✓ $= 2227\cdot8$ ✓ $D = 47\cdot2\,\text{km}$ ✓	4	Find required angle. Use cosine rule.	C
24	a) $123 - 62 = 61°$ ✓ $PD = \dfrac{3}{4} \times 15 = 11\cdot25$ miles ✓ $PE = \dfrac{3}{4} \times 17 = 12\cdot75$ miles ✓ $DE^2 = 11\cdot25^2 + 12\cdot75^2 - 2(11\cdot25)$ $\qquad (12\cdot75)\cos 61$ $= 150$ ✓ $DE = 12\cdot25$ miles ✓	8	Calculate distances travelled in 45 minutes. Use cosine rule.	>C

Question	Expected answer	Mark	Commentary	Demand
24 *(continued)*	**b)** $\cos D = \dfrac{(11 \cdot 25^2 + 12 \cdot 25^2 - 12 \cdot 75^2)}{2(11 \cdot 25)(12 \cdot 25)}$ ✓ $\qquad = 0 \cdot 414$ ✓ $\qquad D = 65 \cdot 6$ $66 - 62 = 4°$ ✓ Bearing $= 180 - 4 = 176°$ ✓		Use cosine rule to find missing angle. Subtract 62 (Z angle). Calculate bearing.	
25	**a)** $PQR = 30$ (Z angle) $+ (180 - 155) = 55°$ ✓ ✓ **b)** Angle $P = 75°$, Angle $R = 50°$ ✓ $\qquad \dfrac{QR}{\sin 75} = \dfrac{8}{\sin 50}$ ✓ $\qquad QR = \dfrac{8 \sin 75}{\sin 50}$ ✓ $\qquad\quad = 10 \cdot 1\,\text{km}$ ✓	6	Use Z angle and angles on a straight line. Find angles at P and R (angles in a triangle $= 180°$). Use sine rule.	C
26	Angle $FHG = 113°$ ✓ $FG^2 = 40^2 + 15^2 - 2(40)(15)\cos 113$ ✓ $\qquad = 2294$ ✓ $FG = 48\,\text{km}$ ✓	4	Calculate internal angle. Use cosine rule. Calculate FG^2.	C
27	**a)** Angle $APK = 100 - 32 = 68°$ ✓ $\qquad AK^2 = 35^2 + 90^2 - 2(35)(90)\cos 68$ ✓ $\qquad\quad = 6965$ ✓ $\qquad AK = 83 \cdot 5\,\text{km}$ ✓ **b)** $\cos A = (35^2 + 83 \cdot 5^2 - 90^2)/2(35)(83 \cdot 5)$ ✓ $\qquad = 0 \cdot 0166$ ✓ $\qquad$ Angle $A = 89°$ ✓ $\qquad 89 - 32 = 57$ ✓ $\qquad$ Bearing $= 180 - 57 = 123°$ ✓	9	Calculate internal angle. Use cosine rule. Use cosine rule to find angle. Subtract 32 (Z angle). Subtract 57 from 180 to get bearing.	>C

Statistical and numerical skills

Surds

Question	Expected answer	Mark	Commentary	Demand
1	$\sqrt{48} - 2\sqrt{3}$ $= \sqrt{16 \times 3} - 2\sqrt{3}$ ✓ $= 4\sqrt{3} - 2\sqrt{3}$ $= 2\sqrt{3}$ ✓	2	Express $\sqrt{48}$ in terms of factors of $48\,(16 \times 3)$. One factor to be a perfect square.	C
2	$\sqrt{72} + \sqrt{2} - \sqrt{18}$ $= \sqrt{36 \times 2} + \sqrt{2} - \sqrt{9 \times 2}$ ✓ $= 6\sqrt{2} + \sqrt{2} - 3\sqrt{2}$ ✓ $= 4\sqrt{2}$ ✓	3	Express $\sqrt{72}$ in terms of factors of $72\,(36 \times 2)$. Express $\sqrt{18}$ in terms of factors of $18\,(9 \times 2)$. Simplify.	C
3	$\sqrt{18} + \sqrt{50}$ $= \sqrt{9 \times 2} + \sqrt{25 \times 2}$ ✓ $= 3\sqrt{2} + 5\sqrt{2}$ ✓ $= 8\sqrt{2}$ ✓	3	Simplify each surd. Add.	C

Question	Expected answer	Mark	Commentary	Demand
4	$\sqrt{2}(\sqrt{10}-\sqrt{2})$ $=\sqrt{20}-2$ ✓✓ $=2\sqrt{5}-2$ ✓	3	Multiply into bracket. Simplify surds.	C
5	$\dfrac{4}{\sqrt{3}}\times\dfrac{\sqrt{3}}{\sqrt{3}}$ ✓ $=\dfrac{4\sqrt{3}}{3}$ ✓	2	Multiply by $\dfrac{\sqrt{3}}{\sqrt{3}}$.	C
6	$\dfrac{13}{\sqrt{24}}\times\dfrac{\sqrt{24}}{\sqrt{24}}$ ✓ $=\dfrac{13\sqrt{24}}{24}$ $=\dfrac{13\times2\sqrt{6}}{24}$ ✓ $=\dfrac{13\sqrt{6}}{12}$ ✓	3	Multiply top/bottom by root 24. Simplify root 24. Cancel.	>C

Indices

Question	Expected answer	Mark	Commentary	Demand
7	$8^{\frac{2}{3}}$ $=\sqrt[3]{8^2}$ ✓ $=2^2$ $=4$ ✓	2	Write as root and power. Take root. Raise to power.	>C
8	$32^{\frac{3}{5}}$ $=\sqrt[5]{32^3}$ ✓ $=2^3$ $=8$ ✓	2	Write as root and power. Take root. Raise to power.	>C
9	$a^{\frac{1}{2}}(a^{\frac{1}{2}}+a^{-\frac{1}{2}})$ $=a^1+a^0$ ✓✓ $=a+1$ ✓	3	Add indices when multiplying. $a^0=1$.	>C
10	$\dfrac{y^3\times y^2}{y^{-2}}$ $=\dfrac{y^5}{y^{-2}}$ ✓ $=y^{5--2}$ ✓ $=y^7$ ✓	3	Add indices. Subtract indices when dividing. Remember $--=+$.	C
11	$t^{\frac{1}{2}}\left(t^{\frac{3}{2}}+\dfrac{1}{t}\right)$ ✓ $=t^2+t^{-\frac{1}{2}}$ ✓	2	Multiply in to bracket. Simplify.	>C
12	3^0+4^{-1} $=1+\dfrac{1}{4}$ ✓ $=1\frac{1}{4}$ ✓	2	Recognise 'to power of 0'. Recognise writing −ve power as +ve power.	C

Question	Expected answer	Mark	Commentary	Demand
13	$E = mc^2$ $= 4 \cdot 2 \times 10^{-2} \times 9 \times 10^{16}$ ✓ $= 37 \cdot 8 \times 10^{14}$ ✓ $= 3 \cdot 78 \times 10^{15}$ ✓	3	Square both parts of $c = 3 \times 10^8$. Express in standard form.	C
14	$C = \pi D$ $= 2 \times 3 \cdot 14 \times 5 \cdot 78 \times 10^7$ ✓ $= 36 \cdot 3 \times 10^7$ ✓ $= 3 \cdot 63 \times 10^8$ ✓	3	Substitute into formula. Calculate. Rewrite appropriately.	> C

Percentages

Question	Expected answer	Mark	Commentary	Demand
15	$5500 \times 1 \cdot 038^4$ ✓ ✓ $= 6384 \cdot 871$ ✓ $= £6384 \cdot 87$ $= £6384 \cdot 87 - 5500$ $= £884 \cdot 87$ ✓	4	State the multiplier. Calculate the index. Calculate total. State the interest.	C
16	$36\,000 \times 1 \cdot 07^3$ ✓ ✓ $= 44\,101.5$ ✓ $= 44\,100$ tonnes to 3 s.f. ✓	4	State multiplier and index. State unrounded answer. State rounded answer.	C
17	$12\,500 \times 0 \cdot 887^4$ ✓ ✓ $= 7737 \cdot 568$ $= £7737 \cdot 57$ ✓	3	State the multiplier. Calculate the index. Final mark for rounding.	C
18	$200 \times 0 \cdot 85^5$ ✓ ✓ $= 88 \cdot 7 \, \text{mg}$ ✓	3	State the multiplier. Calculate the index. Final mark for rounding.	C
19	$345 \, \text{mg} = 115\%$ ✓ $100\% = 345 \div 115 \times 100$ ✓ $= 300 \, \text{mg}$ ✓	3	Identify that $345 \, \text{mg} = 115\%$. Divide by 115, multiply by 100.	C
20	$£336 = 120\%$ ✓ $100\% = 336 \div 120 \times 100$ ✓ $= £280$ ✓	3	Identify that $£336 = 120\%$. Divide by 120. Multiply by 100.	C
21	$£2750 = 112 \cdot 5\%$ ✓ $100\% = 2750 \div 112 \cdot 5 \times 100$ ✓ $= 2444 \cdot 44$ ✓ $= £2440$ to 3 s.f. ✓	4	Identify 112.5%. Divide by 112.5. Multiply by 100. State unrounded answer. Round.	C
22	$£3620 = 114\%$ ✓ $100\% = 3620 \div 114 \times 100$ ✓ $= 3175 \cdot 4$ ✓ $= £3180$ to 3 s.f. ✓	4	Identify 114%. Divide by 114 multiply by 100. State unrounded answer. State rounded answer.	C
23	$£3215 = 92\%$ ✓ $100\% = 3215 \div 92 \times 100$ ✓ $= 3494 \cdot 57$ ✓ $= £3495$ ✓	4	Identify $1 - 0 \cdot 08 = 0 \cdot 92$. Identify 100%. Round as appropriate.	C

Question	Expected answer	Mark	Commentary	Demand
24	£9525 = 77% ✓ 100% = 9525 ÷ 77 × 100 ✓ = 12 370·13 ✓ = £12 400 to 3 s.f. ✓	4	Identify 77%. Divide by 77 multiply by 100. State unrounded answer. State rounded answer.	C

Fractions and mixed numbers

Question	Expected answer	Mark	Commentary	Demand
25	$5{\cdot}03 + 2{\cdot}81 \times 20$ $= 5{\cdot}03 + 56{\cdot}2$ ✓ $= 61{\cdot}23$ ✓	2	Correct order of operations. Calculate total.	C
26	$56{\cdot}4 - 1{\cdot}23 \times 30$ $= 56{\cdot}4 - 36{\cdot}9$ ✓ $= 19{\cdot}5$ ✓	2	Correct order of operations. Calculation.	C
27	$1\frac{2}{3} + 4\frac{3}{4}$ $= \frac{5}{3} + \frac{19}{4}$ $= \frac{20}{12} + \frac{57}{12}$ ✓ $= \frac{77}{12}\left(\text{or } 6\frac{5}{12}\right)$ ✓	2	Convert to improper fractions. Calculate.	C
28	$4\frac{1}{6} + \frac{5}{6} \times 2\frac{3}{5}$ $= 4\frac{1}{6} + \frac{5}{6} \times \frac{13}{5}$ ✓ $= 4\frac{1}{6} + \frac{13}{6}$ ✓ $= 6\frac{2}{6}$ $= 6\frac{1}{3}$ ✓	3	Use improper fractions. Order of operations. Solve.	C
29	$7{\cdot}21 - (7{\cdot}16 - 2{\cdot}04)$ $= 7{\cdot}21 - 5{\cdot}12$ ✓ $= 2{\cdot}09$ ✓	2	Order of operations. Calculate.	C
30	$\frac{2}{7}\left(1\frac{3}{4} + \frac{5}{8}\right)$ $= \frac{2}{7}\left(\frac{19}{8}\right)$ ✓ $= \frac{19}{28}$ ✓	2	Do brackets first (order of operations). Multiply fractions.	C

Standard deviation and interquartile range

Question	Expected answer	Mark	Commentary	Demand
31	Mean $= 324 \div 9 = 36$ ✓ $sd = \sqrt{\left(\frac{380}{8}\right)}$ $= \sqrt{47{\cdot}5}$ ✓ $= 6{\cdot}9$ marks ✓	3	Calculate the mean. Substitute in the formula. Remember to take the square root.	C

Question	Expected answer	Mark	Commentary	Demand
32	**a)** Mean = 650 ÷ 5 = £1·30 ✓ **b)** sd = $\sqrt{\dfrac{0 \cdot 0218}{4}}$ ✓ = £0·07 ✓	3	Calculate the mean. Substitute in the formula. Remember to take the square root.	C

33	**a)** Mean = 27·6 seconds ✓
	
	    sd = $\sqrt{\dfrac{44 \cdot 84}{7}}$ ✓
	
	    = 2·53 seconds ✓
	
	b) On average the girls' times were slower but were more consistent ✓ ✓
		5	The answer should include 'on average …'	C

34	**a)** Mean = 55 kg ✓ **b)** sd = $\sqrt{\dfrac{552}{6}}$ ✓ ✓ = 9·6 kg ✓ **c)** On average the weights of all 6th year were greater and were less varied ✓ ✓	6	Calculate mean. Calculate standard deviation. Make appropriate comments to include 'on average …'.	C

35	47, 48, 49, 52, 53, 55, 56, 57, 57, 60 ✓
	
	SIQ = $\dfrac{(Q_3 - Q_1)}{2}$
	
	    = $\dfrac{57 - 49}{2}$ ✓
	
	    = $\dfrac{8}{2}$
	
	    = 4 ✓
		3	Put in order.
			Find Q_1 and Q_3.
				C

Scattergraphs

Question	Expected answer	Mark	Commentary	Demand

36	**a)** $M = mA + c$
	    $m = \dfrac{5 \cdot 5 - 4 \cdot 5}{15 - 10}$
	    = 0·2 ✓
	    $M = 0 \cdot 2A + c$
	    $4 \cdot 5 = 0 \cdot 2(10) + c$ ✓
	    $c = 2 \cdot 5$ ✓
	    $M = 0 \cdot 2A + 2 \cdot 5$ ✓
	b) $M = 0 \cdot 2(9) + 2 \cdot 5$
	    = 4·3 metres ✓
		5	Calculate gradient.
			Substitute values of M and A into equation of line to find c.
			
			State complete equation with correct labels.
			
			Substitute value of A.
				C

37	**a)** $C = mA + c$
	    $m = \dfrac{80 - 50}{7 - 4} = 10$ ✓
	    $C = 10A + c$
	    $50 = 10(4) + c$ ✓
	    $c = 10$ ✓
	    $C = 10A + 10$ ✓
	b) $C = 10(2) + 10$
	    = 30p ✓
		5	**a)** Calculate gradient.
			Substitute values of C and A into equation to find c.
			State equation with correct labels.
			
			b) Substitute value of A.
				C

Paper 1 (non-calculator)

Duration: 1 hour 15 minutes

Total marks: 50

Attempt ALL questions.

You may NOT use a calculator.

Full credit will be given only to solutions which contain appropriate working.

State the units for your answer where appropriate.

Write your answers clearly in the spaces provided in this booklet. Additional space for answers is provided at the end of this booklet. If you use this space you must clearly identify the question number you are attempting.

Use **blue** or **black** ink.

Before leaving the examination room you must give this booklet to the Invigilator; if you do not, you may lose all the marks for this paper.

MARKS

1 Evaluate $2\frac{1}{4} \div \frac{5}{6}$. **2**

2 Expand and simplify
$(3x - 2)(x^2 - 3x + 1)$. **3**

3 A is the point $(1, 3, 2)$. **2**

$\overrightarrow{AB}$ is $\begin{pmatrix} 4 \\ 1 \\ -3 \end{pmatrix}$

Write down the coordinates of B.

4 Factorise fully
$3k^2 - 12$. **2**

5 Two forces acting on an object are represented by vectors **a** and **b**. **3**

$\mathbf{a} = \begin{pmatrix} 2 \\ -1 \\ -1 \end{pmatrix} \mathbf{b} = \begin{pmatrix} 6 \\ 3 \\ -1 \end{pmatrix}$

Calculate $|\mathbf{a} + \mathbf{b}|$, the magnitude of the resultant force.

Express your answer as a surd in its simplest form.

6 Prove that the roots of the equation $2x^2 + 5x - 3 = 0$ are real and rational. **3**

7 Write $x^2 + 6x - 5$ in the form $(x + p)^2 + q$. **2**

8 The diagram shows part of the graph of $y = x^2 - 6x - 7$.

A is the point $(-1, 0)$ and B is the point $(7, 0)$.

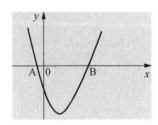

a) State the equation of the axis of symmetry of the graph. **2**

b) Hence, or otherwise, find the minimum value of $y = x^2 - 6x - 7$. **2**

MARKS

9 Evaluate $8^{\frac{4}{3}}$.

2

10 Simplify $\dfrac{3}{k-2} - \dfrac{2}{k}$.

3

11 Mr Barclay bought four adult and two child tickets for a ghost tour.

The total cost was £76.

a) Using a for adult ticket and c for child ticket, write an equation to represent this.

1

Mrs Mackay bought three adult tickets and three child tickets for the ghost tour.

The total cost was £69.

b) Write another equation to represent this.

1

c) Calculate the cost of a ticket for an adult and the cost of a ticket for a child.

4

12 The diagram shows a tiling of congruent triangles.

Vector **u** is represented by $\overrightarrow{AB}$ and vector **v** is represented by $\overrightarrow{AF}$.

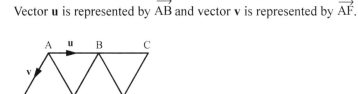

a) Express $\overrightarrow{AD}$ in terms of **u** and **v**.

1

b) Express $\overrightarrow{DB}$ in terms of **u** and **v**.

1

13 Calculate the roots of the equation
$2x^2 + 7x - 15 = 0$.

3

14 Change the subject of the formula $a = b + 2c^2$ to c.

3

15 A line passes through the points A(1, $-t$) and B(3, $5t$) as shown.

Find the gradient of the line, in terms of t.

2

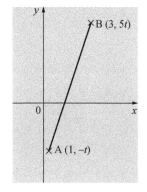

16 Solve the equation $\dfrac{2x}{3} - \dfrac{5}{6} = 2x$.

3

17 Part of the graph of $y = a \cos x° + b$ is shown below.

Explain how you can tell from the graph that $a = 3$ and $b = 1$.

2

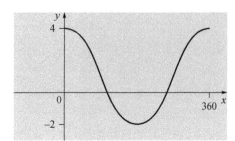

18 In the right-angled triangle shown, BC, the hypotenuse, is 2 units in length.

Side AC is $2 \sin x°$ units in length.

Show that side AB is $2 \cos x°$ units in length.

3

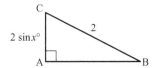

[End of Paper 1]

Paper 2

Duration: 1 hour 50 minutes

Total marks: 60

Attempt ALL questions.

You may use a calculator.

Full credit will be given only to solutions which contain appropriate working.

State the units for your answer where appropriate.

Write your answers clearly in the spaces provided in this booklet. Additional space for answers is provided at the end of this booklet. If you use this space you must clearly identify the question number you are attempting.

Use **blue** or **black** ink.

Before leaving the examination room you must give this booklet to the Invigilator; if you do not, you may lose all the marks for this paper.

MARKS

1 The number of bees in a colony is increasing by 8% per week.

There were originally 1800 bees in the colony.

How many bees will be in the colony after three weeks?

3

2 The diagram shows part of the graph of

$y = (x + a)^2 + b$.

Write down the values of a and b.

2

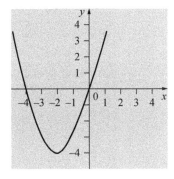

3 In triangle KLM, KL = 10 centimetres, angle MKL = 100° and angle KML = 30°.

Calculate the length of LM.

3

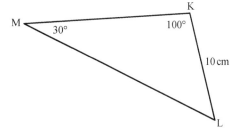

4 A glass paperweight is made in the shape of a hemisphere with a cone on top, as shown in the diagram.

The glass paperweight is 6 centimetres wide and 10 centimetres high. Calculate the volume of the glass paperweight.

Give your answer correct to 2 significant figures.

5

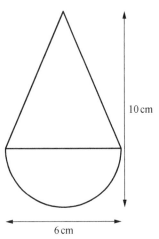

10 cm

6 cm

5 A car I bought last year depreciated in value by 15%.

It is now worth £12 500.

What was it worth when I bought it?

Give your answer to the nearest £100.

4

6 Window panes are in the shape of a rhombus.

The side of each rhombus is 30 centimetres long.

The obtuse angle is 110° as shown.

Find the area of one window pane.

4

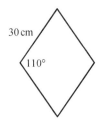

30 cm

110°

7 Brian looked at the price of a tin of baked beans in six local shops.

The costs, in pence, were

52, 48, 57, 46, 54, 49

a) Calculate the mean and standard deviation for this data.

3

Brian checked prices of the tins of baked beans at local supermarkets and found that the mean price was 49 pence and the standard deviation 2·7 pence.

b) Make two valid comparisons between the two sets of data.

2

8 A straight line has equation $3x - 2y + 4 = 0$.

Find the gradient and the y-intercept of the line

3

9 Shampoo is available in **travel** size and **salon** size bottles

The bottles are mathematically similar

The travel size contains 200 millilitres and is 12 centimetres in height

The salon size contains 1600 millilitres.

Calculate the height of the salon size bottle

3

10 The landing area for a discus in a discus-throwing competition is as shown.

The diameter of the circle is 2·5 metres.

The angle at the centre is 35°.

The length of each 'arm' is 25 metres from the centre of the circle.

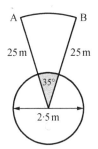

a) What is the area of the shaded sector in the circle?

3

b) What is the length of the outer arc AB?

3

11 A wooden frame has measurements as shown.

Is the frame in the shape of a right-angled triangle?

Show your working to justify your answer.

3

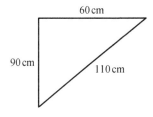

MARKS

12 A lifeboat, L, picks up a distress call from a fishing boat, F, 42 kilometres away on a bearing of 110°.

At the same time another call from a sailing boat, S, comes in.

The sailing boat is at a distance of 16 kilometres from F on a bearing of 230°.

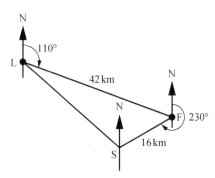

Calculate the distance from the lifeboat to the sailing boat.

5

13 The scattergraph shows the relationship between the age, A (years), and value, V (£000s), of some cars in a showroom.

A line of best fit has been drawn.

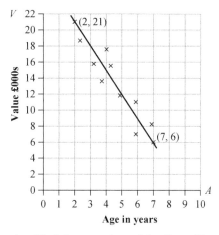

Age in years

a) Find the equation of the line of best fit in terms of V and A.

4

b) Use the equation of the line of best fit to estimate the value of a car which is eight years old.

1

14 a) Solve algebraically the equation

$2 \sin x° - 1 = 0$ for $0 < x < 360$.

3

b) Hence, or otherwise, solve the equation

$2 \sin \frac{1}{3} x° - 1 = 0$ for $0 < x < 360$.

2

15 The diagram shows a circle, centre C.

The radius of the circle is 17 centimetres.

A is the mid-point of chord PQ.

The length of AB is 27 centimetres.

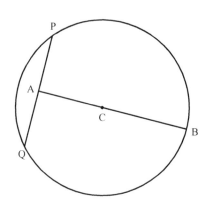

Calculate the length of PQ.

Give your answer to 3 significant figures .

4

[**End of Practice Paper A**]

Paper 1 (non-calculator)

Duration: 1 hour 15 minutes

Total marks: 50

Attempt ALL questions.

You may NOT use a calculator.

Full credit will be given only to solutions which contain appropriate working.

State the units for your answer where appropriate.

Write your answers clearly in the spaces provided in this booklet. Additional space for answers is provided at the end of this booklet. If you use this space you must clearly identify the question number you are attempting.

Use **blue** or **black** ink.

Before leaving the examination room you must give this booklet to the Invigilator; if you do not, you may lose all the marks for this paper.

MARKS

1. Evaluate $1\frac{2}{3} + \frac{4}{7}$. **2**

2. Factorise fully
   $25a^2 - 9b^2$. **2**

3. Evaluate $125^{\frac{2}{3}}$. **2**

4. Multiply out the brackets and simplify:
   $m^{\frac{1}{2}}(m^{\frac{1}{2}} - m^{-\frac{1}{2}})$ **2**

5. A right-angled triangle has dimensions as shown. **2**

   Calculate the length of AB, giving your answer as a surd in its simplest form.

   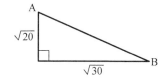

6. Change the subject of the formula $k = \sqrt{\dfrac{a}{b}}$ to a. **2**

7. The area of a circle is $\dfrac{16}{\pi}$ cm^2. **4**

   Show that the circumference of the circle is 8 centimetres.

8. Given $f(x) = 5 - x^2$, evaluate $f(-3)$. **2**

9. Express as a single fraction $\dfrac{1}{x} + \dfrac{2}{x-1}$. **3**

10. Express $\sqrt{125} - 4\sqrt{5}$ as a surd in its simplest form. **2**

11. In triangle ABC, AB = 6 cm and $\sin A = 0.75$. **4**

    The area of triangle ABC = 18 cm^2.

    Calculate the length of AC.

    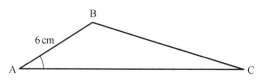

12 The Umbrella Company uses a parabola for its 'U' logo.

The equation of the parabola is $y = (x - 3)^2 - 4$.

Part of the graph is shown in the diagram.

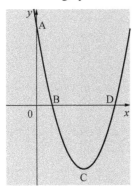

a) State the coordinates of the turning point C.   **2**

b) State the coordinates of point A, where the graph cuts the y-axis.   **1**

c) Calculate the length of the line BD.   **3**

13 The graph below shows two straight lines.   **4**

$y = 2x - 3$

$x + 2y = 14$

The lines intersect at point P.

Find, **algebraically**, the coordinates of P.

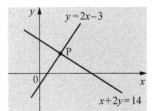

14

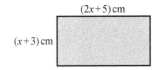

a) Write down an expression, in terms of x, for the perimeter of the rectangle.   **1**

b) The perimeter of the rectangle is equal to the perimeter of the square.   **2**

Form an equation and find the value of x.

c) By how much is the area of the square greater than the area of the rectangle?   **1**

15   ABCDEF is a regular hexagon, with centre G as shown in the diagram.

$\overrightarrow{AB}$ represents the vector **p**.

$\overrightarrow{CD}$ represents the vector **q**.

Find $\overrightarrow{BD}$ in terms of **p** and **q**.

2

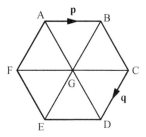

16   Simplify $\dfrac{b^2 + 2b}{5b + 10}$.

3

17   The graph of the function $f(x) = 2x + 3$ passes through the points $(-4, b)$ and $(a, 11)$.
Determine the values of a and b.

3

[End of Paper 1]

Paper 2

Duration: 1 hour 50 minutes

Total marks: 60

Attempt ALL questions.

You may use a calculator.

Full credit will be given only to solutions which contain appropriate working.

State the units for your answer where appropriate.

Write your answers clearly in the spaces provided in this booklet. Additional space for answers is provided at the end of this booklet. If you use this space you must clearly identify the question number you are attempting.

Use **blue** or **black** ink.

Before leaving the examination room you must give this booklet to the Invigilator; if you do not, you may lose all the marks for this paper.

MARKS

1 A light year, the distance light travels in one year, is approximately $5 \cdot 88 \times 10^{12}$ miles.

There are approximately $3 \cdot 15 \times 10^7$ seconds in one year.

How far does light travel in one second?

Give your answer in scientific notation, correct to 3 significant figures.

3

2 Find the equation of the line shown in the diagram.

3

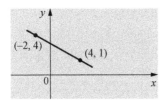

3 A fan is in the shape of a sector of a circle, as shown.

The radius is 14 centimetres.

The angle at the centre is $130°$.

Calculate the perimeter of the fan.

4

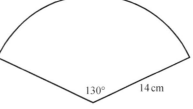

4 Show that

$$\frac{\sin^2 x°}{(1 - \sin^2 x°)} = \tan^2 x°.$$

2

5 Solve the equation

$2x^2 - 3x - 7 = 0.$

Give your answer correct to 2 significant figures.

4

MARKS

6   A group of students sat a maths test.

Their marks, out of 50, were

14, 23, 42, 12, 46, 13, 48, 32, 33, 47

    a)   Calculate the median and the semi-interquartile range of these marks.   3

    b)   A second group of students had a median mark of 28 and a semi-interquartile range   2
        of 21 marks.

        Make two valid comparisons of the marks scored by the two groups of students.

7   A glass ornament is in the shape of a cone partly filled with water.   5

The cone is 22 centimetres high and has a base diameter of 30 centimetres.

The coloured water is 14 centimetres deep and measures 8 centimetres across the top.

What is the volume of water? **Give your answer correct to 2 significant figures.**

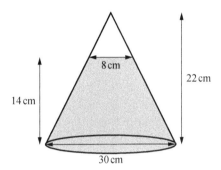

8   A triangle has dimensions as shown.   3

Calculate the size of angle x.

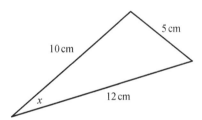

9   Two rectangular solar panels, A and B, are mathematically similar.   4

Panel A has a diagonal of 90 centimetres and an area of 4020 square centimetres.
A salesman claims that panel B, with a diagonal of 125 centimetres, will be double the area of panel A. Is this claim justified? **Show all your working.**

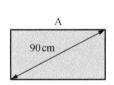 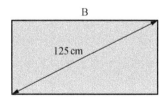

10 Solve the equation   3

$3\sin x° + 2 = 0$ for $0 \leq x \leq 360$.

MARKS

11 The diagram shows vectors **u** and **v**.
Find the components of **u** + **v**.

2

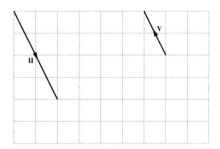

12 A computer cost £360 after VAT at 20% had been added.
What was the cost of the computer before VAT was added?

3

13 A cylindrical water tank, of diameter 120 centimetres, is partly filled with water.
The depth of the water is 25 centimetres.
What is the width of the water surface, AB?

4

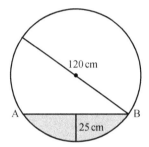

14 Hillwalker B is 400 m due East of hillwalker A.
The two hillwalkers take the bearing of a tree from each of their positions, as shown.
From hillwalker A the tree is on a bearing of 045°.
From hillwalker B the tree is on a bearing of 305°.
How far is it to the tree from the nearest hillwalker?

5

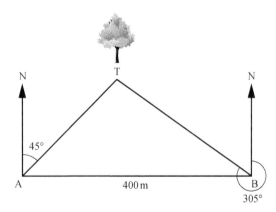

15 The diagram represents a pyramid ABCDE.

The height, EF, of the pyramid is 7 centimetres.

The base is a rectangle with length 6·3 centimetres and width 3·2 centimetres

Calculate the length of the sloping edge, marked x.

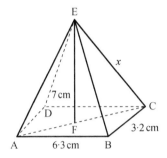

16 Two spotlights are fixed to a beam above a stage in a theatre.

One spotlight has an angle of depression of 37° and the other has an angle of depression of 46°.
Calculate the height, h metres, of the beam above the stage.

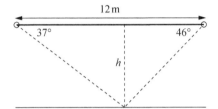

[End of Practice Paper B]

Practice Paper A

Paper 1 (non-calculator)

Question	Expected answer	Mark	Commentary with hints and tips	Demand
1	$\dfrac{9}{4} \div \dfrac{5}{6}$ $= \dfrac{9}{4} \times \dfrac{6}{5}$ ✓ $= \dfrac{54}{20}$ $= \dfrac{27}{10}$ ✓	2	Write mixed number as improper fraction. To divide, invert fraction and multiply. Solution (does not simplify further).	C
2	$(3x - 2)(x^2 - 3x + 1)$ $= 3x(x^2 - 3x + 1) - 2(x^2 - 3x + 1)$ ✓ $= 3x^3 - 9x^2 + 3x - 2x^2 + 6x - 2$ ✓ $= 3x^3 - 11x^2 + 9x - 2$ ✓	3	Split first bracket. Cannot use FOIL as there are three terms in second bracket. Multiply out brackets. Collect like terms.	C
3	$\begin{pmatrix} 1 \\ 3 \\ 2 \end{pmatrix} + \begin{pmatrix} 4 \\ 1 \\ -3 \end{pmatrix} = \begin{pmatrix} 5 \\ 4 \\ -1 \end{pmatrix}$ ✓ B(5, 4, −1) ✓	2	Use vector. State in coordinate form.	C
4	$3k^2 - 12$ $= 3(k^2 - 4)$ ✓ $= 3(k^2 - 2^2)$ $= 3(k - 2)(k + 2)$ ✓	2	Take out common factor. Identify difference of two squares. Factorise fully. When factorising check for: • common factor • difference of two squares • trinomial / quadratic.	> C
5	$\mathbf{a} + \mathbf{b} = \begin{pmatrix} 8 \\ 2 \\ -2 \end{pmatrix}$ $|\mathbf{a} + \mathbf{b}|^2 = 64 + 4 + 4$ ✓ $\qquad\qquad = 72$ $|\mathbf{a} + \mathbf{b}| = \sqrt{72}$ ✓ $\qquad\qquad = 6\sqrt{2}$ ✓	3	Use Pythagoras in 3D to find $|\mathbf{a} + \mathbf{b}|^2$. Take the square root to find the magnitude. Simplify the surd.	C
6	$b^2 - 4ac$ $= 5^2 - 4(2)(-3)$ ✓ $= 49$ ✓ 49 > 0 AND perfect square. Therefore two real, distinct and rational roots ✓	3	Use the discriminant. Correctly substitute a, b, c. Interpret result. Reminder: • $b^2 - 4ac = 0$: equal roots • $b^2 - 4ac > 0$: two real distinct roots • $b^2 - 4ac < 0$: no real roots.	C
7	$x^2 + 6x - 5$ $(x + 3)^2 - 5 - 9$ ✓ $(x + 3)^2 - 14$ ✓	2	$\dfrac{1}{2}$ of x coefficient. Complete solution.	C

Question		Expected answer	Mark	Commentary with hints and tips	Demand
8	a)	$x = 3$ ✓✓	2	Find mid-point of AB and equate to x.	C
	b)	$y = 3^2 - 6(3) - 7$ ✓ $= -16$ ✓	2	Axis of symmetry is mid-point of line joining zeros. Substitute into formula. Evaluate.	C
9		$\sqrt[3]{8^4}$ $= 2^4$ ✓ $= 16$ ✓	2	Rewrite with roots and powers. It is usually easier to calculate the root first.	> C
10		...... $k(k-2)$ ✓ $\dfrac{3k - 2(k-2)}{k(k-2)}$ ✓ $\dfrac{k+4}{k(k-2)}$ ✓	3	Identify correct denominator Identify numerator simplify	> C
11	a)	$4a + 2c = 76$ ✓	1	Form equation.	C
	b)	$3a + 3c = 69$ ✓	1	Form second equation.	C
	c)	$12a + 6c = 228$ $6a + 6c = 138$ ✓ $6a = 90$ $a = 15$ ✓ $b = 8$ ✓ Adult ticket is £15. Child ticket is £8. ✓	4	Set up simultaneous equations (e.g. eqn 1 × 3 and eqn 2 × 2). Find value of one variable. Find value of second variable. Ensure question is answered (i.e. do not just leave values of a and b).	C
12	a)	$\overrightarrow{AD} = \overrightarrow{AB} + \overrightarrow{BE} + \overrightarrow{ED}$ $= \mathbf{u} + \mathbf{v} + \mathbf{u}$ $= 2\mathbf{u} + \mathbf{v}$ ✓	1	Find path. State in terms of $\mathbf{u}$ and $\mathbf{v}$.	C
	b)	$\overrightarrow{DB} = \overrightarrow{DE} + \overrightarrow{EB}$ $= -\mathbf{u} - \mathbf{v}$ ✓	1	2D vectors question. Find the path by looking for lines parallel to given vectors. (Other paths could be used.)	C
13		$(2x - 3)(x + 5) = 0$ ✓✓ $x = \dfrac{3}{2}$ or $x = -5$ ✓	3	1 mark for each bracket. 1 mark for solutions.	> C
14		$a = b + 2c^2$ $a - b = 2c^2$ ✓ $\dfrac{a - b}{2} = c^2$ ✓ $\sqrt{\dfrac{a - b}{2}} = c$ ✓	3	Subtract b. Divide by 2. Take square root. In a changing the subject question, do one step at a time.	> C
15		$m = \dfrac{5t + t}{3 - 1}$ ✓ $= \dfrac{6t}{2}$ $= 3t$ ✓	2	Use gradient formula. $m = \dfrac{y_2 - y_1}{x_2 - x_1}$	> C

Question	Expected answer	Mark	Commentary with hints and tips	Demand
16	$4x - 5 = 12x$ ✓ $-8x = 5$ ✓ $x = -\dfrac{5}{8}$	3	Multiply by 6 (or equivalent). Rearrange (collect like terms). State solution.	> C
17	$a =$ amplitude $= 3$ ✓ $b = 1$ (graph moved up 1 square) ✓	2	Amplitude $\dfrac{1}{2}$ 'top to trough'. Difference from −2 to 4 is 6. Therefore amplitude is half of 6.	C
18	$AB^2 = 2^2 - (2\sin x)^2$ ✓ $\quad = 4 - 4\sin^2 x$ $\quad = 4(1 - \sin^2 x)$ ✓ $\quad = 4\cos^2 x$ $AB = \sqrt{4\cos^2 x}$ $\quad = 2\cos x$ ✓	3	Use Pythagoras' theorem. Use the identity $\sin^2 x + \cos^2 x = 1$.	> C

Paper 2 (calculator)

Question	Expected answer	Mark	Commentary with hints and tips	Demand
1	$1800 \times 1 \cdot 08^3$ ✓ ✓ $= 2267$ ✓	3	Use multiplier of $1 \cdot 08$. Power of 3. $(100\% + 8\% = 108\% = 10 \cdot 8)$	C
2	$a = 2$ ✓ $b = -4$ ✓	2	Graph moved 2 left (halfway between −4 and 0 is −2). Graph moved 4 down.	C
3	$\dfrac{LM}{\sin 100} = \dfrac{10}{\sin 30}$ ✓ $LM = \dfrac{10 \sin 100}{\sin 30}$ ✓ $= 19 \cdot 7 \, cm$ ✓	3	Use sine rule. Rearrange. Calculate solution.	C
4	$V = \dfrac{1}{2}\left(\dfrac{4}{3}\pi r^3\right) + \dfrac{1}{3}\pi r^2 h$ ✓ $= \dfrac{2}{3}\pi(3^3) + \dfrac{1}{3}\pi(3^2)(7)$ ✓ $= 122 \cdot 5$ ✓ $= 120 \, cm^3 \,(2 \text{ s.f.})$ ✓	5	Use formulae for volumes of hemisphere + cone. Substitute values, including correct radius (half of 6 cm = 3 cm). Calculate (unrounded). Round correctly.	C
5	$85\% \rightarrow 12\,500$ $100\% \rightarrow 12\,500 \times \dfrac{100}{85}$ ✓ ✓ $= 14\,705$ ✓ $= £14\,700$ (nearest £100) ✓	4	Set up 'proportion'. Set up calculation. Perform calculation. Round correctly.	C
6	Use area of triangle formula. Area $= \dfrac{1}{2}bc \sin A$ ✓ $= \dfrac{1}{2}(30)(30)\sin 100$ ✓ $= 443 \cdot 16 \,(\times 2)$ ✓ $= 886 \cdot 3 \, cm^2$ ✓	4	Clearly state formula. Substitute values. Calculate area of triangle. Double.	C

Question		Expected answer	Mark	Commentary with hints and tips	Demand
7	a)	Mean = 51p ✓ $$\sum(x-\overline{x})^2 = 84 \checkmark$$ $$\text{s.d.} = \sqrt{\frac{84}{6-1}} = 4 \cdot 1\text{p} \checkmark$$	3	Find the mean. Find total of $(x-\overline{x})^2$. Substitute into formula.	C
	b)	On average supermarkets were cheaper and more consistently priced. ✓✓	2	Include 'on average'. Comment on both mean and standard deviation but do not use those terms. In your comparisons you should refer to the prices. Do not say, for example, 'the mean is lower' or similar.	C
8		$$3x - 2y + 4 = 0$$ $$-2y = -3x - 4$$ $$y = \frac{3x}{2} + 2 \checkmark$$ Gradient $= \dfrac{3}{2}$ y-intercept $(0, 2)$	3	Rearrange. State gradient. State y-intercept.	> C
9		Vol sf $= \dfrac{1600}{200} = 8 \checkmark$ Linear sf $= \sqrt[3]{8} = 2 \checkmark$ Height of salon size $= 12 \times 2$ $= 24$ centimetres $\checkmark$	3	Calculate Volume scale factor. Calculate linear scale factor. Calculate height.	> C
10	a)	Area of sector $$= \frac{35}{360} \times \pi \times 1 \cdot 25^2 = 0 \cdot 48 \text{ m}^2 \checkmark\checkmark\checkmark$$	3	Substitute into formula, using correct radius and angle.	C
	b)	Arc $= \dfrac{35}{360} \times \pi \times 2 \times 25 \checkmark\checkmark$ $= 15 \cdot 3 \text{ m} \checkmark$	3	Substitute into formula, using correct diameter. In arc and sector questions, check carefully that you have used the correct angle AND the correct radius/diameter.	C
11		Use Pythagoras' theorem. $90^2 + 60^2 = 11\,700 \checkmark$ $110^2 = 12\,100$ $90^2 + 60^2 \neq 110^2 \checkmark$ ∴ by converse of Pythagoras' theorem it is NOT a right-angled triangle. ✓	3	1 mark for calculating $90^2 + 60^2$. 1 mark for comparing with 110^2. 1 mark for conclusion. Note when using converse of Pythagoras do not start by saying $90^2 + 60^2 = 110^2$. You cannot assume they are equal. Take each 'section', then compare.	C

Question		Expected answer	Mark	Commentary with hints and tips	Demand
12		$f^2 = l^2 + s^2 - 2ls\cos F$ $\quad = 16^2 + 42^2 - 2(16)(42)\cos 60$ ✓ $\quad = 1348$ ✓ $f = 36{\cdot}7$ km ✓	5	Use the cosine rule. Substitute in F, l and s. Find length f.	C
13		$m = \dfrac{21-6}{2-7} = -3$ ✓ $y - b = m(x - a)$ $y - 21 = -3(x - 2)$ ✓ $y = -3x + 27$ ✓ $V = -3A + 27$ ✓ $V = -3(8) + 27 = 3$ Value = £3000 ✓	5	Find the gradient. Substitute gradient and one point in general equation of straight line. Write in context of V and A. Substitute into formula. Calculate value.	C
14	a)	$\sin x = \dfrac{1}{2}$ (angle in first and second quadrants) ✓ $x = 30$ ✓ $x = 150$ ✓	3	Rearrange equation to $\sin x =$. Find solution in first quadrant. Find second solution.	C
	b)	$\sin \dfrac{1}{3}x = \dfrac{1}{2}$ $\dfrac{1}{3}x = 30,\ 150$ ✓ $x = 90,\ 450$ $x = 90°$ ✓	2	Use results from part a). $450°$ is out of range.	> C
15		Know to use Pythagoras. E.g. draw line CP. $AC = 27 - 17 = 10$ ✓ $AP^2 = CP^2 - AC^2$ $\quad = 17^2 - 10^2$ ✓ $\quad = 189$ $AP = \sqrt{189} = 13.7(..)$ ✓ $PQ = AP \times 2$ $\quad = 13.7(..) \times 2$ $\quad = 27.4(..)$ ✓	4	Marshal facts and recognise right angled triangle. E.g. Consistent Pythagoras statement. Calculate AP. Calculate length of chord.	> C

Practice Paper B

Paper 1 (non-calculator)

Question	Expected answer	Mark	Commentary with hints and tips	Demand
1	$\dfrac{5}{3} + \dfrac{4}{7}$ $= \dfrac{(35+12)}{21}$ ✓ $= \dfrac{47}{21} = 2\dfrac{5}{21}$ ✓	2	Write mixed number as improper fraction. Correct denominator.	C
2	$25a^2 - 9b^2$ $= (5a)^2 - (3b)^2$ ✓ $= (5a - 3b)(5a + 3b)$ ✓	2	Write as difference of two squares and factorise fully. When factorising check for: • common factor • difference of two squares • trinomial/ quadratic.	> C
3	$125^{\frac{2}{3}}$ $= 5^2$ ✓ $= 25$ ✓	2	Take cube root. Square. When working with fractional powers, it is usually easier to do the root first, then the power.	> C
4	$m^{\frac{1}{2}+\frac{1}{2}} - m^{\frac{1}{2}+-\frac{1}{2}}$ $= m - 1$ ✓✓	2	Apply the laws of indices. Simplify. Make sure you know the laws of indices, e.g. $m^0 = 1$.	> C
5	$AB^2 = \left(\sqrt{20}\right)^2 + \left(\sqrt{30}\right)^2$ ✓ $= 20 + 30$ $= 50$ $AB = \sqrt{50}$ ✓ $= 5\sqrt{2}$ ✓	3	Use Pythagoras' theorem. Simplify the surd.	C
6	$k^2 = \dfrac{a}{b}$ ✓ $bk^2 = a$ ✓	2	Square both sides. Multiply by denominator.	> C
7	$A = \pi r^2$ $\dfrac{16}{\pi} = \pi r^2$ ✓ $16 = \pi^2 r^2$ $\dfrac{4}{\pi} = r$ ✓ $C = 2\pi r$ $= 2\pi \dfrac{4}{\pi}$ ✓ $= 8$ ✓	4	Use area formula to find r. Substitute for r in circumference formula.	> C

Question		Expected answer	Mark	Commentary with hints and tips	Demand
8		$f(x) = 5 - x^2$ $f(-3) = 5 - (-3)^2$ ✓ $\quad = -4$ ✓	2	Correct substitution for x. You should recognise function notation and know how to find a value.	C
9		$\dfrac{1}{x} + \dfrac{2}{x-1}$ $= \dfrac{x-1+2x}{x(x-1)}$ ✓ ✓ $= \dfrac{3x-1}{x(x-1)}$ ✓	3	State common denominator. Correct numerator. Simplify.	C
10		$\sqrt{125} - 4\sqrt{5}$ $= \sqrt{(25 \times 5)} - 4\sqrt{5}$ ✓ $= 5\sqrt{5} - 4\sqrt{5}$ $= \sqrt{5}$ ✓	2	Split surd. When simplifying a surd, look for perfect squares.	C
11		$\text{Area} = \dfrac{1}{2} bc \sin A$ $= \dfrac{1}{2} \times AC \times 6 \times 0 \cdot 75$ ✓ $18 = \dfrac{1}{2} \times AC \times 6 \times 0 \cdot 75$ ✓ $2 \cdot 25 \times AC = 18$ $AC = 18 \div 2 \cdot 25$ ✓ $= 8\,\text{cm}$ ✓	4	Substitute into area formula. Form equation. Rearrange to make AC the subject.	C
12	a)	$(3, -4)$ ✓ ✓	2	Use $(x - a)^2 + b$.	C
	b)	$(0, 5)$ ✓	1	Substitute $x = 0$ into equation of curve.	C
	c)	$(x - 3)^2 - 4 = 0$ ✓ $(x - 3)^2 = 4$ $x - 3 = \pm 2$ $x = \pm 2 + 3$ $x = 1, x = 5$ B $(1, 0)$, D $(5, 0)$ ✓ BD $= 4$ ✓	3	Substitute $y = 0$ into equation of curve. Rearrange. Find both values of x. Find coordinates of B and D. State length of BD.	C
13		$y = 2x - 3$; $x + 2y = 14$ ✓ $x + 2(2x - 3) = 14$ $5x = 20$ $x = 4$ ✓ $y = 2(4) - 3$ $y = 5$ ✓ P $(4, 5)$ ✓	4	Substitute for y in second equation. Find first variable. Find second variable. State coordinates of P. Note that the question states 'algebraically', so do not use a geometry approach.	C

Question		Expected answer	Mark	Commentary with hints and tips	Demand
14	a)	Perimeter $= (2x + 5 + x + 3) \times 2$ $= 6x + 16$ ✓	1	(Length + breadth) $\times 2$	C
	b)	Perimeter square $= 4(3x + 1)$ ✓ $= 12x + 4$ $12x + 4 = 6x + 16$ $6x = 12$ $x = 2$ ✓	2	Form equation. Find solution.	C
	c)	Difference = area of square − area of rectangle $= 49 - 45$ $= 4\,\text{cm}^2$ ✓	1		C
15		$\overrightarrow{BD} = \overrightarrow{BG} + \overrightarrow{GC} + \overrightarrow{CD}$ ✓ $= \mathbf{q} + \mathbf{p} + \mathbf{q}$ $= \mathbf{p} + 2\mathbf{q}$ ✓	2	Find suitable path. Look for equivalent vectors. State vector pathway.	> C
16		$\dfrac{b(b+2)}{5(b+2)}$ ✓ ✓ $= \dfrac{b}{5}$ ✓	3	Factorise top and bottom. Cancel $b + 2$.	> C
17		$f(x) = 2x + 3$ $f(-4) = 2(-4) + 3 = -5$ $b = -5$ ✓ $f(x) = 2x + 3$ $11 = 2x + 3$ ✓ $x = 4$ $a = 4$ ✓	3	Substitute -4 for x. State value of b. Substitute 11 for $f(x)$. State value of a.	C

Paper 2 (calculator)

Question	Expected answer	Mark	Commentary with hints and tips	Demand
1	$(5 \cdot 88 \times 10^{12}) \div (3 \cdot 15 \times 10^{7}) = 18\,6666 \cdot 6$ ✓ ✓ $= 1 \cdot 87 \times 10^{5}$ ✓	3	Set up division and divide. Answer in scientific notation to 3 significant figures.	C
2	$m = \dfrac{(1-4)}{(4+2)}$ $= -\dfrac{1}{2}$ ✓ $y - b = m(x - a)$ $y - 1 = -\dfrac{1}{2}(x - 4)$ ✓ $y = -\dfrac{1}{2}x + 3$ ✓	3	Calculate gradient. Substitute values into formula. Simplify. This is a straight-line question, so you need the gradient and one point on the line.	C

Question		Expected answer	Mark	Commentary with hints and tips	Demand
3		$\text{Arc} = \dfrac{130}{360} \text{ of circumference}$ $\text{Arc} = \dfrac{130}{360} \times \pi \times d \checkmark$ $= \dfrac{130}{360} \times \pi \times 28 \checkmark$ $\text{Perimeter} = \text{arc} + 2 \times \text{radii} \checkmark$ $= 31.8 + 28$ $= 59.8 \text{ cm} \checkmark$	4	Correct fraction. Substitute into formula. Correct method. Solution. This is a typical arc question. Look carefully at the wording – here you need to find the perimeter, not just the length of the arc.	C
4		$\dfrac{\sin^2 x}{(1 - \sin^2 x)} = \dfrac{\sin^2 x}{\cos^2 x}$ $= \left(\dfrac{\sin x}{\cos x} \right)^2 \checkmark$ $= \tan^2 x \checkmark$	2	Identify $1 - \sin^2 x = \cos^2 x$. Identify $\dfrac{\sin x}{\cos x} = \tan x$. There are two identities you need to know: $\sin^2 x + \cos^2 x = 1$ and $\dfrac{\sin x}{\cos x} = \tan x$.	> C
5		$2x^2 - 3x - 7 = 0$ $a = 2, \ b = -3, \ c = -7 \checkmark$ $x = \dfrac{-b \pm \sqrt{b^2 - 4ac}}{2a} \checkmark$ $x = \dfrac{3 \pm \sqrt{(-3)^2 - 4(2)(-7)}}{2(2)}$ $x = \dfrac{3 + \sqrt{65}}{4} \text{ or } \dfrac{3 - \sqrt{65}}{4} \checkmark$ $x = 2.766 \text{ or } -1.266$ $x = 2.8 \text{ or } -1.3 \text{ (to 2 s.f.)} \checkmark$	4	Substitute into quadratic formula. Evaluate $b^2 - 4ac$. Unrounded roots. Rounded roots. The wording 'give your answer correct to 2 significant figures' implies the equation will not factorise easily so you need to use the formula. Remember to write your unrounded answers, and then round.	C
6	a)	Median $32.5 \checkmark$ $Q^1 = 14, \ Q^3 = 46 \checkmark$ $\text{SIQR} = \left(\dfrac{46 - 14}{2} \right) = 16 \checkmark$	3	Median. Q1 and Q3. Semi-interquartile range.	C
	b)	The second group's marks were lower on average and they were more varied. $\checkmark \checkmark$	2	Valid comment regarding median. Valid comment regarding semi-interquartile range. To find median and quartiles, remember to write the list in order.	C